C000142682

In Place of Schools

"Do not confine your children to
your own learning for they were
born in a different time"

(Old Hebrew Proverb)

For:

June, Jane and Rachel

Acknowledgements:

During forty years many students, teachers and writers
must have contributed to the ideas contained in this book,
and I am grateful to them all, but I would like to thank particularly those who read and commented on the script,
including   Frank Adcock, John Bastiani, Peter Davies,
Colin Duckworth, Barry Jones, Alan Langton, Janet
Meighan, Roland Meighan, Jane Randall and Gerald
Rimmington. Responsibility for the final text and all that is
in it is, of course, mine.

IN PLACE OF SCHOOLS

... a novel plan for the 21st Century

John Adcock

FOREWORD BY
Roland Meighan

ILLUSTRATIONS BY
Penelope Jane Randall

NEP   New Education Press Ltd   1994

© John Adcock 1994
First published 1994

ISBN 0-946947-62-7

British Library Cataloguing in Publication Data:
A catalogue record for this book is available
from the British Library.

Copyright, Designs & Patents Act, 1988:

Apart from any fair dealing for the purposes
of research or private study, or criticism or
review, as permitted under the Copyright,
Designs and Patents Act, 1988, this
publication may be reproduced, stored or
transmitted, in any forms or by any means,
only with the prior permission in writing of the
publishers, or in the case of reprographic
reproduction in accordance with the terms of
licences issued by the Copyright Licensing
Agency. Inquiries concerning reproduction
outside those terms should be sent to the
publishers at the undermentioned address.

This book is sold subject to the condition that
it shall not, by way of trade or otherwise, be
lent, re-sold, hired out, or otherwise circulated
without the publisher's prior consent in any
form of binding or cover other than that in
which it is purchased and without a similar
condition being imposed on the subsequent
purchasers.

All the characters and events described in
this book are fictitious and any resemblance
to any person, living or dead, or to any actual
event, is entirely coincidental.

Now published by:
AMS Educational (NEP)
Low Lane, Horsforth
Leeds LS18 5NY   27 Old Gloucester

Telephone: 0113 258 0309
Printed by:
Adlard Print & Typesetting Services, The Old
School, Village Green, Ruddington, Nottingham
NG11 6HH

A Foreword

The American writer and award-winning teacher, John Gatto, observes that a significant result of compulsory, mass schooling is that even amongst the best of his fellow teachers, and amongst even the best of his students' parents, only a tiny number can imagine a different way to do things.

John Adcock is amongst the tiny number of teachers who can imagine a different way. His tale is set in the year 2029 when the reforms begun in 1999 have been running for some time. The tutors in the new flexible system appear to be somewhat puzzled as to why the previous antiquated and regressive system took so long to lose credibility and collapse.

The tale is told with wit and humour. It is a pleasure to read not only because of its compelling storytelling, but because it is created with considerable plausibility out of a close observation of the current trends in society. Thus, he has some awareness of the trail blazed by the brave, nonconformist, pioneering families who opt for home-based education and find, often to their surprise, that it is highly successful.

John Adcock sees much change as derived from accidents, crises and opportunism. Key decisions depend on the turn of a committee chairman's coin - by now an ECU. He sees the technological change and the various revolutions in communications as developing with a somewhat relentless logic, but suggests this will create opportunities for increased family involvement in education.

Nothing in the tale is to be construed as criticism of teachers or their work in the 1990s. The position is taken that thousands of caring and humane people work in schools but the logistics of a system without conscience overwhelms their individual contributions. Everett Reimer proposed that some true educational experiences are bound to take place in schools, but they occur despite school and not because of it. Although many teachers work very hard, the institution is mean-spirited.

Predicting the future is easy. Getting the prediction right is the problem. The only way to make any judgement in this case is to set to and read John Adcock's splendid, entertaining and thought-provoking tale.

Roland Meighan
Special Professor of Education, University of Nottingham

A Preface

Although this story is a fanciful sortie into a future world of alternative education, it is based on a set of plausible developments of our 20th Century lifestyle :-

- an expansion of the electronic media which will increase the range of educational material available in every home.
- a rise in the amount of non-working time available to the bulk of the adult population.
- the willingness of the nation to consider alternatives to the current school-based system of teaching.
- the provision, within 21st Century housing-improvement programmes, of well-equipped study rooms in every home.
- a desire to see children remaining largely within the family for their early education, given that there is ...
- the professional help of personal tutors for all parents and their children.

Some of these developments are already occurring and, given the present pace of social and technological change, the others may be with us soon. This could provide a golden opportunity to try alternative ways of teaching, apart from those which are school-based. The 130-year-old approach might still be best for some teachers and children and preferred by some parents, but different arrangements might benefit others greatly.

The idea in this story, *In Place of Schools*, could, with some adaptation, be tried now. A nation as wealthy as Britain, with its immense reservoir of talent, its history of world leadership and its large, compact population, could easily afford and successfully establish several fully resourced educational systems running side by side for an adequate trial period. This would give parents a real choice in the education of their children and offer teachers an opportunity to discover whether their skills and efforts could bring for everyone greater reward.

J.A., September 1994

Note: Throughout this book tutors are referred to as 'she' and pupils as 'he'. This is to avoid the tedious repetition of 'he or she', 'him or her' and 'his and hers'. It is not an indication that in 2029 there will be no male tutors or female pupils.

Susan Smith, Personal Tutor

It is Friday, 28th December in the year 2029. The hour is 0808 EST (European Standard Time). Susan Smith checks this on her personal computer screen together with the local weather and traffic news, and her day's appointments.

Susan, born in the first hour of the first day of the first year of the 21st century, is a professional personal tutor to nineteen children aged from eight to ten years.

She tutors the children with their parents, or in small groups, in their homes, in her home, in community resource centres, in field stations, in museums and art galleries, in concert halls and theatres, in libraries and sports centres, and in other places where, in her professional opinion, advantage to her clients will accrue.

Susan is not a teacher in the 19th or 20th Century sense of the word. She does not teach in a school. There are no teachers and there are no schools. There are simply personal tutors, pupils, parents, and extensive support facilities.

Susan possesses, for each of the children in her tutorial group, a personal study programme. She devised each programme with the help of the child, his parents, and colleagues' notes on the child's earlier achievements. She did this before the child first came to her from his previous tutor at the age of eight. The programme outlines the child's studies for the next two years and Susan reviews it each month - again with the help and concurrence of the child's family. She calls on help from colleagues and such other support agencies as she feels are needed. She then sets a detailed study programme for the child for the days immediately ahead.

Susan takes responsibility for the appropriateness of each on-going programme. This is her professional task: sound educational 'prescriptions' for her clients and the acceptance of full responsibility for the efficacy of what she prescribes.

Susan Smith is happy in her work. She can think of no other career she would rather have. She is benefiting, as are her fellow tutors, her pupils, their parents and the whole of society, from quite desperate decisions made about education in the dying months of the last century. Those decisions were made reluctantly and implemented spasmodically. They came as a result of two factors combining to force a decision: the realisation that after 130 years the school-based system of teaching had run its course, and that rapidly-evolving technology, combined with personal tuition, presented a viable and possibly far superior alternative.

What the school could offer, with individual teachers working largely alone in classrooms, was meagre compared with the vast choice of material emanating from the electronic media. Satellite transmissions from all over the world, fibre optic cable, multi-channelled television and radio, and sophisticated facsimile machines, had made possible the despatch and reception of an immense range of programmes, lessons, experiences and responses to almost any place at any time. All could be supported by supplementary material and background notes for adult and child at any level of comprehension. This had been barely imaginable only a generation earlier. Some could not digest the implications, while others chose not to. But changing social circumstances in the nation forced all to examine what lay ahead.

At the turn of the millennium three groups had worked together in haste. These were politicians, amalgamations of worried teachers acting - amazingly - in unison, and parents, anxious to participate in any scheme likely to aid them in the difficult task of bringing up their children. They had all decided that the great potential of the rapidly-developing media should be used to the benefit of society. Particularly it should be utilised in the education of young children. What was needed, they agreed, was a means whereby the skills of the teacher in relating to children could be fully utilised, with the teacher released from the time and energy-consuming tasks of preparing, quite uneconomically, teaching materials. Such a scheme was devised almost fortuitously, and when its implementation began it was seen also that far more had been done for the professional enhancement of teachers than had ever been foreseen or even intended. Everyone had gained.

A huge central library of transmittable material had been created, approved and stored ready for instant retrieval and direct delivery to the homes of tutors, their pupils and their parents and any other citizens who chose to receive it. So vast had the store become and so wide, varied and appealing its range, that within five years it was possible for a knowledgeable tutor to devise a personalised curriculum capable of meeting the individual academic and social needs of each child in her care. A tutor, such as Susan Smith with her eight and nine year olds, could then amend or fine-tune each curriculum as the child's requirements were seen to develop, or the wishes of the parents change.

The media - largely the electronic media - had become the provider of lessons - the 'teacher' of the old school-based system. Part of the personal tutor's work had become the prescription of 'lessons' to be taken and the study that would arise from each. But, as had been laid down by a far-seeing member of the parliamentary select committee which had devised the new system, the reading of literature, selected and aided by a tutor who now had the time and skills necessary for the work, would be an intrinsic element in any curriculum and have priority over anything else that was included.

Thus, from the moment such media potential was understood and the means of utilising it within a viable personal-tutoring system was devised, the days of the traditional school and classroom were numbered. Social problems, which in some schools had grown acute by late 1999, precipitated the movement. Then, seen in terms of educational change, the end was remarkably swift. By 2020 all but a very few of the old-fashioned schools had gone and the institution's 150 year life had drawn to a close. There had been few mourners at the graveside. Many a teacher, near to the end of her tether, had been glad to see it buried. The memorial headstone, paid for many times over by generous public subscription, had read simply:

The School, 1870-2020.
It lived beyond its years.

To Susan Smith this was part of recent social history. Most schools had gone long before 2020 and she herself had not been taught in one. To her, schools were places her parents had attended and from one of which her father, a sensitive man, a teacher of music, had taken the most welcome of early retirements. Despite all the skills and talents he had had to offer, he had become disillusioned and exhausted at fifty-four.

This educational transformation had been forced on a conservative society. It had not been planned eagerly or carefully long in advance. But it had meant that the Susan Smiths of late 2029 were able to enjoy a fulfilling career free of the school's physical restrictions, hierarchical structure and disciplinary fears.

Many had not seen the transformation in those terms. They feared that much would be lost if the school disappeared: the guidance of a good headteacher, the support of an interested and talented governing body, the incentives offered to teachers by an in-built system of promotion, the fine social entity that was said to be the hallmark of an excellent school.

But not all headteachers were effective leaders, some governing bodies lacked drive and expertise, some observers saw the promotion system for teachers as fatally flawed, some schools lacked the fine social cohesion that might justify their long-term retention.

Many other facets of the school were mourned only briefly: the rectangular dimensions of many glass, brick and concrete class-rooms planned decades earlier for a standard thirty bodies; the 'school day' frequently and often insensitively segmented by the shrill tones of a remotely-controlled bell; the long-drawn-out school terms of mediaeval origins; the abundance of paperwork which took up so much time and nervous energy; the distant London ministries absorbed daily by statistics for this and statistics for that. Few tears had been shed for any of these.

In 2029 Susan Smith rarely thought of that era. She was, as so many teachers in the old school-based system had never had the chance to become, a fully fledged, independent professional person, working in a role comparable with the long-established professions. As a result of the changes instigated years before she qualified, she had never been a salaried employee executing a fixed curriculum under the guidance or control of examination boards. She had not been required to test her charges on the learning of material she had not devised or selected, nor had she been inspected - no matter how kindly or fleetingly - within a system which could not know sufficiently her long-term aims or her short-term problems.

Now, the tutor of 2029 accepted responsibility for what she did. She had professional oversight of the educational wellbeing of the twenty children in her care. She was answerable for what was done, face to face, with her pupils and their families. The buck stopped with her. Nor would she wish it any other way for she knew that the essence of her professional status and freedom depended greatly on that. She knew also that, should the need arise, parents and pupils were free to seek tutorship elsewhere, or even, in exceptionally difficult cases, legal redress.

Thus had come the personal professional status that had evaded teachers in the old system since state schools emerged in the 1870's, 80's and 90's. Susan had read about the classroom teacher's relatively low ranking in the old organisation, and of the chain of events that had brought it to an end. But always she had read with a measure of disbelief. The educational world was so different today; how could things have been like that?

Today she was meeting a new pupil, Paul, recently arrived in the area from Luton; she would see him and his parents at 09.00. From 10.00 until 11.00 she would meet a small group of parents and pupils in the study in her own home to talk about the work they had done and ensure they understood what media library programmes they were to view next and the work that would follow. Then she would visit Jennifer, Alan and Christine at Jennifer's house to discuss a drama they were preparing after listening to a series of radio broadcasts: Jennifer's mother thought the broadcasts had been difficult and the follow-up work too taxing.

At noon each day Susan tried to be available in the local community resource centre for informal meetings with any pupil, parent or colleague who wished to see her. Then, also at the centre, in a comfortable restaurant, she would take lunch at 13.15 with a parent who was offering to help with the introduction of a leisure area in which several pupils had shown an interest and in which Susan considered herself weak. In the afternoon she would spend much time finalising arrangements with a tutor-panel colleague for a combined visit by twelve children to a nearby field station for three days: they were preparing for a longer visit to South Wales on which would be based a major topic on Roman military and domestic life in the second and third centuries and the literature of those times. An elderly gentleman, recently retired from educational work, was to accompany them to give of his expertise.

At the same resource centre she would then be meeting four pupils, individually, in a quiet reading area, for an hour or more. At 17.45 she would discuss a progress report on Timothy Frett, aged ten, with the boy and his father before the report was placed formally on permanent file. At 19.30, Susan and three other tutors from her practice, or panel, would view and assess new material made available from the National Media Library (NML) at Melton Mowbray.

Twenty-nine-year-old Susan Smith would thrive on every minute of the day. At the end she would feel much had been accomplished. Professionally, she would feel fulfilled, and, because of the high level of work satisfaction she achieved, her clients would benefit, too. Tutoring children in this way, where she planned her day and organised her pupils' programmes individually and with varying but considerable family participation made for a fascinating and wholly enjoyable career. Unlke some teachers in the old system, so she had been told, she was able to look forward to her work and gain daily pleasure from it.

Sometimes Susan was puzzled. She wondered how the old-style teachers had tolerated their working conditions and practices for so long. From what she had heard the schools had imposed what, to her, would be intolerable constraints. She saw herself akin to a medical doctor in general practice: she belonged to a panel, she had her consulting room or study where she saw parents with or without their children, she made home visits, she had a resource centre which she viewed as a community educational 'hospital', and the NML which was the supplier of materials, ideas and research. But, following a university tutorial, her tutor had urged her not to push the analogy too far!

Quietly she started her car ready to drive to Paul's new house, pondering this point. She tapped in the 'road advised' code on the in-car computer and glanced at the 'best route available' shown on the screen. She thought again of the old-style teachers and pondered further. Even less explicable than *how* they had tolerated school-based teaching was *why* they had tolerated it. Had not an alternative been staring everyone in the face? She moved gently into the traffic - silent and virtually fume-free. But the important thing, she thought, was that they had been shown an alternative in the end, and had pursued it happily. Changes had been made.

Yet it was not the teachers as a body who had devised the new system, nor was it the administrators, or the parents. It had come about partly by chance and partly through the persistence of a young doctor of philosophy of London University who had seen the opportunities and then seized them with all the guile and vigour of the keen educationalist and astute politician he was.

The transformation from classroom teacher to personal professional tutor and from national curriculum to individual study programmes had not been accomplished smoothly. It had not been carefully devised. It had not been recognised as an exciting innovation. It had been brought about by unadulterated political expediency. In some areas there had been a desperate need to try something different: to try anything that might work. Then, months before the young doctor of philosophy arrived on the educational scene, there had been a fortuitous family visit to the USA by a British middle-ranking, middle-aged politician. This politician had not been an educationalist either in spirit or practice, but a wily man who saw a way out of a mess for his party, a possible means of saving money for the taxpayer, and a chance to gain career kudos for himself. It was, in other words, a prime example of how much change comes about. Yet good had come of the process in this instance for millions of children.

All this had happened shortly before Susan Smith was born. Accounts of events varied - from those which tried seriously to document the entire course of the changes to those which, while bizarre and amusingly anecdotal, nevertheless gave some insight to the truth. During professional training Susan and her college friends had enjoyed the latter type, and one leading lecturer on their tutor preparation course, a youngish lady with several television comedy scripts to her credit, had spiced her discourse with a helping of humour and more than a splash of imagination !

During a cold winter seminar in 2022 she told them that towards the end of the century the control of pupils in many classes in some schools had been stretched to breaking point. Truancy was rife. School arson and vandalism were common. Requests for early retirement flooded in from all spheres of the teaching force - from disillusioned classroom teachers who had 'done badly' in the pro-motion race to more senior teachers and administrators who were perceived to have 'done well'. Clerical chores had proliferated at the expense of direct teacher-pupil contact time. Trouble had been ongoing over curriculum matters and the testing of children on materials not welcomed by the teachers and over whose inclusion they claimed to have had little say; they had been required to administer tests not devised by them and which they viewed with distaste, or even dismay.

"The History of Education" had no formal part in professional tutors' courses of the 21st Century, but Susan's particular lecturer thought it important that students should know something of the dramatic events that had immediately preceded the teaching-without-schools era they now enjoyed. She usually introduced it to her small group of postgraduate students over coffee.

Susan thought it sounded awful. Even teachers' salaries, she learned, had ceased to be the main bone of contention by the late 1990's. This was something unprecedented on the educational scene as pay disputes had been to the fore ever since the turbulent post-war days of 1945. This was not because teachers had, by 1999, gained an enviable affluence, but because dissatisfaction with the job itself had taken over as the main cause of complaint.

Successive political leaders had thrown into the simmering soup a few pet ingredients of their own and stirred the mixture gingerly, but it had been to no avail: education had reached the point when it needed more than a different flavour. History teachers knew how Nero had fiddled . . . while the restaurant burned down. So did the more enlightened of parents who wondered, increasingly, what was happening to the education of their children. Some, despairing of the schools altogether, had kept them away, deciding they could do better for their children by educating them at home.

Susan's tutor had lowered her voice over-dramatically at this point, as if to emphasise her next remarks. She said the great danger that had arisen in the final decade was one of apathy and acquiescence on the part of many educationalists. They had appeared punch-drunk from all the changes that had been forced on them. They seemed ready to settle for anything provided it meant a respite from the perpetual reorganisations that had dogged their careers for a decade or more.

"The teachers' response to unwelcome and seemingly discredited changes was probably pernicious in its effects, for teachers began to think they had had enough of new ideas. But," and she paused to ensure her students' attention, "in fact there had been no really radical changes at all. There had been no stimulating ideas. There had been nothing that had called for a fundamental rethink of what education was all about. The multiplicity of changes, which teachers were so understandably tired of, were really no more than a tinkering with the old system's tatty peripherals . . ."

The leading lecturer argued that there had been no new ideas, in essence, since the 1870s when children were taken, by law, from their homes and taught, compulsorily, in classes in schools. For over a hundred years western nations had persisted with this same rudimentary practice when the original need for it had long since passed.

She claimed that the structure of the 1990s' school was basically the same as it had always been. There were headteachers and assistants, with pupils placed in groups in classes and taught in classrooms by a solitary teacher for a set period of time in buildings set apart from the wider community. She then suggested that all that had been intermittently composed between the early 1870s and the late 1990s had been an uninspiring set of variations on an old Victorian educational theme.

Individual teachers had gained little, if anything, in professional standing in all that time. They were still under the direct supervision of others, often teaching lesson content devised and prescribed by boards who did not know the children personally, and still hampered by paperwork. It was, she held, this rapidly worsening scenario that led to the abandonment of much of the school-based system in 1999 and its hurried replacement by an alternative arrangement based on the personal tutoring of children. Fortunately, and despite the haste, the remedy had worked remarkably well.

Susan had been enthralled by the story: it could well have been a pseudo-scientific fiction from an earlier era. She would have liked to have observed all these changes first hand - but not to have participated!

The leading lecturer had continued eagerly. She knew this was always a popular topic, and she was a little guilty at times of embroidering her tale.

"On the ninth day of the ninth month of 1999," she said, ". . . an easy date for us to remember . . . the end came. The school-based structure began its collapse, and, as you would have expected had you been there, it was a few of the older and larger secondary schools in the biggest cities that toppled first. The trigger was the belated discovery that there was no money to pay a promised health and safety allowance to teachers working in dangerous localities. At the same time, a proposed scheme to patrol some schools on a twenty-four hour basis to curb violence and vandalism was postponed because plans had not been finalised. Truancy-check teams were withdrawn from the streets because of political in-fighting on councils, and a torrid sex scandal of mind-boggling proportions in the higher echelons of educational administration had focussed popular attention on the teaching scene at the very time it was not wanted.

"In 1999 teachers had been leaving the service in droves and replacement recruits were only dribbling in. A proposal to bring in poorly-qualified staff as 'a temporary measure' had brought the threat of a strike from three major teaching unions - there was no single professional body to represent teachers' interests in those days. Even moderately inclined parents were howling for blood - although they were not quite sure whose - and one militant parents' association was beginning a test-case action to arraign a senior official for failing to provide the quality of service demanded by law. Television and the press were in full cry and the school system - in several areas - finally ground to a halt. Some schools were closed officially as an extension to the summer holiday, others simply did not bother to re-open. Three junior government ministers returned hurriedly from exotic vacations abroad and even that event was seized upon hysterically by the media because, in her haste, one picked up the wrong baggage in Mexico City and was questioned in Spanish by puzzled officials!"

The leading lecturer checked, as good story-tellers should, that her students were sitting comfortably - one had fetched more coffee - and continued with the saga.

"Along came bold Sir Sing-Along Strain - a member of parliament in late middle age. He had been visiting an American aunt in Old School Creek and had half-heard, while his aunt dozed, a speaker on one of the American television networks talking about alternative education. Sir Sing-Along was not quite sure what that was, but the speaker, whose deep Southern accent did not help the good knight's efforts to comprehend, seemed to be lauding the practice of home-based teaching. Apparently a huge number of American families - the man talked of a million - had chosen to teach their children at home and did not send them to schools. Evidently the practice had grown in other countries, too, and was making significant strides in Britain.

"Sir Sing-Along was not sure how this was done, or why, but gathered, from the fragments he heard, that there were several variations - single family teaching, groups of families, part-time or occasional attendance at regular schools - and so on. But it was possible, Sir Sing-Along gathered, to get by without making use of the customary and costly chain of specially-built and expensively

16

maintained schools.

"This seemed an excellent thing to the tax-conscious member of parliament. He saw that bringing the idea back to the UK might divert attention from the awful trouble that was brewing for his government, save huge sums in taxes, popularise his party and, of course, bring a little glory for himself to boost his as yet singularly indifferent political career.

"On his return, finding the British educational scene in even greater disarray than when he had left for America, he expressed to colleagues his view that what was needed was an alternative.

"Canny and astute though he had always been throughout a long and varied career, Sir Sing-Along could never have imagined how brilliant his timing would be in this situation. It was judicious, propitious, opportune, appropriate . . . it was perfect. He could not believe the idea had occurred to no-one else.

"'An alternative . . .' cried the Cabinet and Shadow ministers, unbelievably in unison. 'We need an alternative.'

"Sir Sing-Along reeled. Suddenly everyone wanted an alternative system for teaching children. That was obviously the way out of their difficulties. And almost anything would do . . .

"'Of course anything will do,' yelled an irate member of the opposition. '. . . anything will be better than the mess we're in now . . .'

"There were groans from all quarters and his attempt to gain party political benefit from the turmoil failed completely. All sides wanted a way out and for once were tacitly agreed that the apportioning of blame and naming of names could wait.

"Anything would do. But what? What *was* the alternative? Sir Sing-Along was thrust forward, bewildered by the response to his tentative suggestion. His own educational achievements had been crowned by a mediocre degree from a modest university and a testimonial from his tutor which had emphasised his social graces.

"He was called on to chair a select committee, and to find some answers quickly and very much in the public eye. But he knew nothing about alternative education, and in desperation decreed that telephone calls - peak-rate and lengthy - should be made to the USA to trace the speaker he had half listened to on the television set in his maiden aunt's air-conditioned room in Old School Creek. For a very substantial fee, the famous professor - he turned out to be an Associate Professor of Alternative Approaches from Alabama - gave again, in London, the gist of his talk. And it proved to be a simple proposal - so simple that the listening politicians understood it easily at first hearing.

"It was that teachers, following a period of retraining in the liberal and language arts, would become personal tutors, practising in small groups, or panels, to a group of children - about twenty to each tutor - and that those tutors would become fully responsible for the educational wellbeing of those children from the ages of four to thirteen. Each would tutor her own group for two years before the children moved on to another tutor, probably within the same practice. The huge sums spent on education would be reduced because there would be vast savings in bureaucracy. The money available would be divided, more or less equally, between the tutor groups doing the work. Some of the money saved, supplemented by sums raised from the sales of schools and their land, would provide a vast library of electronic teaching resources. These would be made available to tutors on a prodigious scale and, using the new technology, tutors would be able to compile personal learning programmes of an interest and level suited to each child in their charge. Parents would become full partners in this compilation and be encouraged to play an increasing part in all aspects of their children's education. That participation would be crucial.

"The go-getting professor from Alabama had paused and surveyed his audience. He had not been sure how they would take his next proposal: some seemed apprehensive already. But he had risked it . . . after all, they were paying him generously.

"He told them that, by government edict, all new houses should have, built-in, a combined study, library, music and art room. It would be light and airy with large windows and be soundproofed to provide a reception area for new, unimaginably realistic transmissions, in quadraphonic sound and 3D vision, of exciting, mind-widening programmes of unlimited choice. And, of course, there would be available there the very latest developments in two-way communications with all parts of the world. That room would become the most important in every home. Older houses would have an extension built on or a conversion made, while unsuitable houses would be swept away in the massive rehousing programmes scheduled for the new millennium. He said a rapidly-falling population, in which small families would become the norm, would ease each nation's housing problem and make agreeable refurbishing of housing stock an entirely viable proposition.

"As he flew home, first class, his fee already credited to his distant account in United States dollars, he wondered what the Brits would make of that. But the Brits had taken it, as Brits do, step by cautious step, and were, by 2022, making steady progress . . ."

Susan and her fellow students contemplated the story quietly.

"And that's how our homes got their studies?"

"More or less. It was ironic. The rich American's ideas were supported by a radical socialist MP, a normally sceptical man," said the leading lecturer. "He demanded that all homes have space for the arts. He said the arts should never be the prerogative of the rich and grandly educated.When told to be realistic, he became angry and said the scoffers should remember how housing had changed even since 1900. Then few homes had bathrooms and indoor toilets. Few had gas, electricity and mains water. Even fewer had garages, conservatories, double glazing or central heating. Putting in a small study would be nothing compared with all that.

"When asked where the money would come from he said the huge sums released by ending the Cold War could do the lot - the money couldn't be put to better use. Every home should have a quiet area where parents and pupils and these new tutors could study."

"That's what he said?" asked a student.

"Yes. And he had them over a barrel. No-one dared be quoted as being opposed to such a laudable objective."

"That's how the tutorial system started?"

"It was a huge factor. But as so much happened at the same time in 1999, it would be wrong to isolate just one cause."

"And they all lived happily ever after?" murmured another friend.

"That is for you to say," replied the leading lecturer.

But Susan had already decided how she would answer. In no way would she have wanted to teach in the system that existed before that magical date of the ninth of the ninth, ninety-nine.

"I know what I think," she said. And so did all the others.

3. A Most Select Committee

1999 was a horrible year for tired politicians. Two general elections in six months had produced two hung parliaments, two hapless coalition governments and a mass of eager new members who filled the lobbies and urged reform.

The incoming prime minister tackled the crisis in education head-on by appointing a select committee to research and recommend alternative approaches. He showed new-broom qualities by appointing only members who were new to the House - and who better to lead such a zealous band than that harbinger of educational innovation, Sir Sing-Along Strain?

The good knight had won his parliamentary seat in a 1996 by-election which was unsurpassed for its thirteen candidates, tactical voting, numerous recounts and rampant ill-will. With three years' service he was the elder statesman of the motley committee he first called to order at 14.30 on Tuesday, 12th October, 1999.

Trouble erupted at 14.45 and Sir Sing-Along's unease at his appointment quickly grew. A proposal to include three co-opted members - all ex-teachers from the old system - to 'keep feet on the ground' was voted down. But significant resignations were threatened and the point was churlishly conceded.

Their nomination had been supported by the high-flying, remarkably young, flaxen-haired ex-county councillor London Ph.D. who had just been elected to fill one of the re-established university seats. He combined academic brilliance with practised political guile, a charmingly persuasive disposition, and a determination to reform the nation's schooling. He and his three ex-teachers were to prove a powerful group in the weeks ahead.

The select committee's first task was to decide whose needs a new system would have to meet. Sir Sing-Along was adamant that needs must be ascertained: he could see little point in budgeting for things that were not actually and immediately required. The clever Ph.D., who was to become the knight's unofficial mentor, did not correct his notion of what 'needs', in this particular context, meant. And so the committee's work began.

Findings or suggestions of just what was needed came from

politicians' mail bags, letters to editors, constituency parties, unions, church leaders, petitionists, lobbyists and the like. They gave the committee plenty to think about and there were some refreshing and surprising suggestions, even when many that were personally and unpleasantly motivated were placed judiciously to one side.

As a result of these revelations, the committee decided to split its work into four areas - and examine distinct sets of 'needs': the needs of the state, the needs of children, the needs of teachers - or tutors - and the needs of the children's parents or guardians.

Immediate objections to this proposal aroused Sir Sing-Along again. A few determined and vociferous members threatened to leave unless the order in which the needs were listed was changed. First were to be placed the needs of the children (although clearly these would in some respects coincide with the needs of the other three groups), then the needs of their parents, then those of the state and, finally, those of the teachers.

"The old school-based system was instigated to satisfy the demands of the state," argued one lady of liberal persuasions. "In the nineteenth century the state needed a semi-literate and semi-numerate workforce and a conforming, well-drilled population. In the 1870's and 80's the industrial revolution had to be carried further - Britain had to prosper and maintain her world lead. So the schools, bleak as they were, gave us 'the three 'R's' and rigid discipline supported by imposed authority. Thus the schools had the buildings and regimes of the factories, mills and offices which their pupils were later to enter. So let's make sure we don't do the same. Let's put the state's needs *after* those of children."

Despite objections forcefully put, the good lady won the day. With her sweet smile and loose, auburn, waist-length hair, she seemed the exact antithesis of a hard-faced politician. But she could stand her ground when a cause was to be defended and so the needs of children were put first. Parents' needs, on examination, were seen to be closely entwined with those of their children, and were placed second. As one politically astute member put it, "they are the voters and taxpayers of the present and the future."

The needs of the teachers, although not to be ignored, were to be put last because they were to be a new professional group in society and as such would be expected to submerge their needs to the needs of their clients:- pupils, parents and state.

On this most select committee the brilliant young member from the Midlands (Middle City, Fringe, South), quietly gained in influence.

He had been a successful sixth-form teacher and held a First in English Literature from London University and a Ph.D from the same institution for his well-publicised 1996-1997 research into the early twentieth-century novelists' perception of childhood as portrayed in contemporary adult fiction. Alert, deep-thinking and well read, any politician more unlike Sir Sing-Along Strain would have been difficult to discover. But the adept academic, realising how far out of his depth the noble knight was, seized, discreetly, each opportunity that came to gain influence. He helped the chairman to avoid traps, to take dangerous corners skilfully and to make light of his educational ignorance. Thus he gained power behind Sir Sing-Along's none-too-stable, hastily-wheeled-out throne.

Next, under the young man's quiet tutelage, and smiled upon benignly by the chairman, the select committee readily accepted that children's needs were not primarily the learning of school-based subjects, or laid-down national curricula, or society-selected skills taught in large, sometimes impersonal classrooms of thirty pupils or more for set slices of time. As many teachers knew, children had greater, deeper more urgent needs than those.

They required an abundance of opportunities for developing warm, long-standing, close relationships with other children in small, secure personal groups. They needed the same with similarly composed groups of caring, non-dominating adults over long periods of time. The need was a deeply-felt one of being wanted: that somebody knew about them and that somebody cared. It was this security, built on sound relationships, that would be the principal contributor to a happily-balanced personality throughout childhood and which would be carried forward into adult life. If that feeling of being wanted was not present, nothing else that was done would matter very much.

So compelling were the young man's arguments, and so supportive the remarks of the three ex-teachers, that the select committee accepted with little dissension the existence of these needs. But in their attempt to embrace them fully they scarcely envisaged the implications of what they were doing. They were clearing the way for the professionalism of the Susan Smiths of 2029 and for a veritable revolution in childhood education.

While they were in receptive mood the idea was pressed on them that a personal-tutor system with a tutor and parent working together with the child would provide the greatest hope of meeting these basic needs. The clever Ph.D from London University was steadily establishing his gains.

And he was artful. He paved the way, easily - almost casually - for what he had in store for the committee when the curriculum itself came up for review. He did not want his forthcoming proposals to be such a shock to the committee then that their stunned resistance would defy his efforts to instigate curricular change.

He hinted, with Sir Sing-Along nodding a none-too-enthusiastic approval, that combined with this steadily-evolving three-part relationship, children would be introduced, gradually and naturally, to a wide variety of interests that would enrich their leisure time. Simultaneously there would be a weakening of the demarcation lines between 'working time' (previously associated by children with hours spent in school) and 'free time' (hours spent out of school). Specific 'working time' he intended to phase out, it being replaced by a proper preparation for the enormously extended periods of 'leisure time' children already experienced, and which most would continue to enjoy increasingly throughout their lives. He was looking to 2029 and far beyond.

The 1999 select committee accepted that an alternative education system would need to ensure that there was both love and care for the child and a gradual widening of his interests. The traditional separation of home and formal education would disappear. The personal tutor would be the facilitator of this change and the instigator of the child's growing range of interests. The Susan Smiths of the future would be the professional guides to the non-material aspects of each child's development. In that way, urged the London Ph.D - frequently manipulating others so that they appeared to speak his words for him - there would be real hope that the child's progression would be stable, balanced and happy in a society where full time and continuous employment seemed unlikely to exist for the bulk of the population.

Select committee members recoiled at this concept despite the gentleness with which it was put. It was difficult to conceive of the outright abandonment of each political party's cherished dream of long-term full employment for all. But the evidence was all around them, and had been there for a long time. Perhaps it was easier on the soul to reflect that many citizens would be spared a lifetime spent in occupations which earlier generations had been forced to follow and which had provided for many workers little more than forty years of ill-paid drudgery.

But none would voice these thoughts. They vacillated, each

waiting for a political opponent to speak first. The economic implications, both for individuals and for society, of an acceptance that at least partial unemployment for many was to become the norm, were either too enormous to grasp or too dangerous to admit.

And there was another fear. How would people spend their time in the coming age of long periods of unemployment, part-time working, early retirement - the coming age of leisure? What would they do? Was it possible for society, by means of a totally different way of preparing young people for the new life, to offer something eminently more worthwhile than a lifetime in the pits, factories, mills and offices? Would it ever be politically - let alone economically - acceptable to suggest that *no* job might be preferable to *some* jobs? Or would that always be heresy?

One of the co-opted teachers spoke, hesitantly, even though he was not politically ascribed and had no party line to follow.

"Do we really suppose," he said to the assembly at large, "that an alternative education system could help create a contented, happy population, only a proportion of whom would work full time? Could it be done? I would like to think it could, but could it?"

"It could," the London Ph.D. assured him, glancing at Sir Sing-Along. The committee also turned to the chairman; he seemed to be in agreement. In fact, they told themselves, the young man seemed to be speaking on his behalf most courteously and well.

"That would be marvellous," the long-haired liberal lady soon conceded. "Marvellous."

The most select committee joined their chairman in his head-nodding. Bald heads, dark-haired heads, heads with fringes and buns, crew cuts, pigtails, perms and expensively-shaped sideburns all nodded: it would be marvellous. They could sell that to the electorate. Everything would be all right.

Reports to the select committee regarding parents' needs were as varied as they were complex. Many parents said some schools had become too much of a rat race with crowded curricula, too-frequent testing, poor discipline, stressed teachers and final and formal examinations on which far too much depended. There had been vying between schools for the attraction of pupils and 'league tables' had been drawn up which attempted to rank schools in accordance with arbitrary performance standards. That had been disgraceful, a tired trades union spokesman said.

Some select committee members sat uncomfortably through this for they knew they had either concurred or done nothing to discredit the systems and get them withdrawn. They had kept quiet when they had known, deep within themselves, that they should have been undaunted in their opposition.

The impression was emerging rapidly that parents would be prepared to abandon the divisively competitive element within the early education years - up to the age of twelve or thirteen - if that meant the meeting of their children's personal and social needs *and* on condition that this would apply to the whole new system; i.e. that one child was not to be disadvantaged because the children of other parents were encouraged to 'race ahead' in the old academic contests.

It was said that parents needed to see their children develop individually in ways they could approve of. And they needed help, when appropriate, in the immensely difficult process of managing their children's personal development. The members accepted the implied criticism that parents had had precious lttle help with this vital task up to now.

"That's right," emphasised a pallid parent-governor and mother of seven. "After the first few months there is little skilled, on-going help or advice, and that, given in a tactful way, is much needed."

"Some wouldn't even thank you for it," said an employers' suave representative, dismissively. "Others wouldn't want to know."

"Perhaps not, at first, but they might eventually. And, anyway, that's no reason for not starting. No reason at all. There would be doubters, even obstreperous people, but hopefully even they would begin to see that those negative attitudes would be costing their children dearly, as well as themselves. They would come to know that, while working at that task of child-rearing - creative and satisfying, but sometimes difficult and frustrating - skilled friendly help would be at hand. I would have given much for that in my time."

Again the Ph.D. kept quiet. He could see that there would be no long-term ideological problem here. But he knew that the main obstacle to his alternative education scheme would be raised by parents who saw the demise of the school as the removal of a childminding facility - one on which they had come to depend. They needed that facility while they went out to work, did the shopping or housework, looked after other family members, or simply took 'time out' from the ever-present and draining demands of child care. Here, he thought, there could be serious problems.

But he would cross that bridge when he came to it. The committee would need shepherding across - the chairman too. It might prove to be a particularly nasty, slippery, hump-backed bridge, and they might come to it at dusk. It could have dangerous bends at either approach, and there could be deep, dark water in the river below. There might even be the odd whirlpool lying undetected, waiting . . . But that was for another day . . . . and he had a strategy ready.

The doctor of philosophy from London University suppressed a sigh of relief at the general agreement on parental needs. He went on to steer the discussion towards the state's needs. He hinted that the needs of a democratic nation were analogous to those of the people living within it. Thus the needs of the nation's children and their parents - and, to a lesser extent, their tutors - became a significant part of the totality of needs within the state. So the needs of people, many of which had already been determined, were the needs of the state. He wanted to avoid the idea that a nation in some way existed by itself, an entity apart from its people, that it possessed needs separate from and in addition to those of its citizens. He wanted the most select committee to keep away from conceptions of an impersonal and non-human nature, such as 'industry' or 'commerce' or 'the armed forces' or 'the church' or 'the electorate', or even such vagaries as 'the people'. That way trouble lay.

But he noted an uneasy stirring to his right, and a shuffling from the nearby Sir Sing-Along Strain. So, as a car salesman might (to all intents and purposes reluctantly) concede that a slightly scratched wing-mirror would be replaced before a £5,000 used car deal was completed, so the young doctor conceded that a nation requires intelligent, responsible citizens - part of a 'work force' that might carry the nation forward and upward.

"They should have the personal resources to enjoy their lives to the full in a variety of ways, having, of course, regard to the legitimate rights of fellow citizens." This he offered as a bartering point, knowing that it would cost him nothing because he shared already the sentiment it expressed.

"Personal responsibility . . . not relying on the state for every damn thing . . ." came from the far right.

"Personal responsibility entirely," the Ph.D. said on behalf of Sir Sing-Along. "That we must have."

He agreed, too, that the state needed citizens who, once they had elected a government, would respect and abide by the laws that government passed even if that meant personal loss or incon-venience to themselves.

"What about the workers?"

The question could have been put by a trades union delegate at an annual conference or by a boss of industry anxious about a lack of skills in his work force. But the tone of voice and the general appearance of the speaker - as well as the side of the table on which he sat - suggested the latter. It was, indeed, the employers' suave leader.

The young Ph.D suggested to the chairman that industry and commerce both needed a happy, resourceful and responsible band of employees which possessed the necessary - and frequently changing - skills of each trade. "But," he murmured to Sir Sing-Along, "any direct preparation for adult work should deliberately, as part of educational policy, be left until a more formal stage of education - when children were fourteen or fifteen, or maybe older."

"Wonderful," whispered the dreamy liberal lady . "Quite, quite wonderful."

"No preparation for work?" queried a conservative lady of more robust and formidable character - one noted more for her shrewd political prowess than for idealism. Her parliamentary majority in her comfortable shire constituency was as substantial as her frame.

"No. Not specifically. It would be preparation for life until then," persisted the liberal lady.

"For life?"

"For a life far beyond mere industry and commerce. An attempt to show children how much more this world can offer than clocking-on and clocking-off, overtime and piecework rates, company dividends and capital gains . . ."

"But . . ."

"Haven't we reached an era when science and technology is enabling us to look, in our own good time, at the overall lifestyle we want to have? And then to go on and give our children those exhilarating opportunities, too?" This last came from the tired trades union spokesman who, unwittingly, had come to the aid of the Ph.D. But this partisan support was not altogether welcomed. He went on:

"There was a time when a ten or twelve hour day, fifty week year, was needed - so the workers were told - to keep the country going. And slavery it was."

He waited for contradictions; there were none. Many members had heard it all before, some at their grandfathers' knees.

"It was then that we established those dreadful nineteenth century schools - to prepare the workforce for that awful life. Now we need neither the workforce nor the drudgery, and we don't need that sort of school either."

He paused. He had failed to convince them, despite the effort.

"That, after all," he said, wearily, "is why this most select committee is sitting - and there's not much that's select about it if you ask me. We're supposed to be considering an alternative to those schools - something better for all our children, not just those of the favoured few." His glance indicated his targets.

A resolute, sixty-year-old business woman and leading executive in the nation's retail food industry - a person wealthy even by Sir Sing-Along's standards - spoke for the first time:

"How many schools have you visited recently?" she asked. "Just what do you think they are like? Are you still in the 1800s?"

The union leader looked at her, almost with a sneer.

"I visited one only last week," he said. "It was closed. It had been set on fire - for the third time. The one next to it had a truancy rate which even that borough is ashamed of. It's closed, too. The schools are finished!" He sat back. He had made his contribution.

The committee seemed to be floundering. It had reached a crisis. Sir Sing Along was troubled. What *were* they trying to do? He could not believe all schools were bad; he was a governor of an excellent school. He now wished he had postponed his visit to the USA. Indeed his sister had suggested that he delay the visit until next year because of pressure of work and the forthcoming election. But their American aunt was ninety-four and frail.

"No schools?" he thought. "No preparation for work? Tutors? He had had tutors at university, and an ill-assorted bunch they had been! *All children* to be taught by *tutors?*

Sir Sing-Along Strain looked around as if seeing the most select committee for the first time. Perhaps he had not grasped the full significance of what was happening, but he was beginning to. Could it be some cunningly concealed attack by the extreme Left Wing - or the extreme Right Wing, or any other despicable gang of dedicated fanatics? An attack on the Establishment, starting with the schools? Insurrectionists sometimes began their dastardly work with onslaughts on the schools and universities. Was he being used as a mouthpiece - the genial and trustworthy statesman, innocently manipulated into lending credibility to their whole crazy scheme? He turned to his mentor, the merest hint of suspicion on his face. But before he could say anything a gruff laboured voice broke in. It was a boring, slow and ponderous voice, one which would register 'arrogant' on any scale of modesty. It was one which was listened to because its audience usually had no option but to listen; not one which would cause all and sundry to turn towards it voluntarily. It belonged to a disliked lawyer.

"Haven't we tried to include both the preparation for work and the preparation for leisure in our schools up to now?" he enquired. But he was not seeking an answer from anyone in the room; the question was put so that he could answer it.

"Can't we have both?" he asked. It was another rhetorical question. "What's wrong with that?"

He forgot for a moment that he was not in court: he had started to rise to his feet. Then he made as if to adjust his gown, and felt undressed and slightly foolish when he realised it was not there. Then, before he could continue his address, the liberal lady, her long hair swinging gently from side to side, asked:

"And with what success? So often we have tried to give both and succeeded in giving neither. Let us all join together and say that the twentieth century has been the century of science and technology and that it has given us so many benefits and such exciting possibilities to enhance our lives. Now let us make use of what science has given us and make the twenty-first century the one in which we all come to life - let us make it the Century of the Arts..."

"Really..."

"Let us be, oh so brave, and say we want all our children to learn about the great things in life - things that will stand them in good stead for ever and ever..."

"Such as?" demanded the disliked lawyer, testily.

"Literature, music, art, sculpture, the very joys of modern ballet..."

"Good grief." The lawyer winced. "Really, Mr Chairman..."

But it was no use. He was unpopular. He carried little sway: he was not in court. If he favoured 'A' most of the committee would vote for 'B'. He subsided, and a sceptical socialist member beamed.

And so the idea that, at least until pupils reached the age of thirteen, the new means of education should emphasise the arts won the day. Members' emotions had been stirred by the liberal lady's eloquent plea and they voted in her favour.

And the most select committee was tired. The proponents of the arts were persistent. And, after all, times were changing. Past records of mixing objectives in the schools had been, as the lady later elaborated, none too successful. Further, as the Ph.D let drop gently when the moment seemed right, the committee was charged with seeking out and reporting back on alternatives. A mere tinkering with the existing system would not do. How they would all be criticised for that ! An alternative was required.

The young Ph.D packed his briefcase contentedly as members of the most select committee rose.

"Well done, Sir Sing-Along," he said encouragingly. "Well done, sir. A most satisfactory preliminary meeting . . ."

"We didn't get on to the needs of teachers . . ." the nervous knight rejoined. He was not happy. He did not like this.

"They were well covered in all the other sound proposals we made," the young man declared, soothingly. "Teachers will accept those as an excellent alternative to what they have now . . . they could hardly do otherwise."

"I suppose so," agreed the gallant gentleman. "At least they won't be any worse off."

He thought ahead to his club, and dinner, and some good brandy. He was a connoisseur of brandies.

"And they haven't much clout, have they? Teachers?" he asked.

"Very little," smiled the young Ph.D and one-time sixth-form master. "Very little. Certainly none you need worry about."

The chairman was reassured. Teachers had no clout.

A New Curriculum

Throughout its many meetings of Autumn 1999, Sir Sing-Along Strain was surprised by the unpredictability of the committee he had been pressed to chair. After the differences that emerged when needs were addressed - differences which had not yet been publicly revealed - the chairman expected bitter disputes over the compilation of curriculum guidelines for personal professional tutors. But none, of any substance, arose.

The select committee and the nation were tired of decades of perceived lawlessness in the streets, contempt for authority on all fronts, money-grubbing in many quarters, petty regulations imposed by armies of well-paid bureaucrats, discipline problems in many of the country's schools, and a philosophy of 'anything goes as long as it makes money'. This last, many felt, had been epitomised by various authorities' repeated failure to tackle earnestly the growth in violence on the screen with all that that seemed to imply about their lack of concern for the healthy development of young people. The nation was ready for sweeping new - genuinely new - measures in the construction of curriculum guidelines for tutors.

Soundings made on behalf of the most select committee confirmed that reappraisal of the nation's morals was sorely needed. Many parents, teachers, school governors, older pupils and other interested parties were decidedly unhappy. As one respondent put it, "Things need tightening up quick." His poor grammar was, in the circumstances, excused.

As far as children's education was concerned, there was a desire for a simple, clearly-stated, readily-understood purpose, and this purpose, or aim, which some respondents did not find easy to express, was that each child should be helped to grow up to be - as far as possible - a happy, interested and interesting adult who would be reasonably content with his life and who would show concern for the lives of others. Respondents could not always see why so simple and straightforward an objective had to be wrapped in educationalists' elaborate jargon or why it should need an army of bureaucrats, legions of administrators and corps of itinerant inspectors to secure its achievement. Nor did they see why the offices of those who did not teach had to be more expensively appointed than the classrooms of those whose work with children was the very *raison d'etre* of the education service. Nor did many understand the wide discrepancies between the salaries of those who administered and those who taught; although they had become accustomed to this anomaly in other care-service fields and a few thought there must be something sacrosanct about the arrangement. The select committee, encouraged by the ex officio teacher members, showed general agreement.

Indeed, so broad was the consensus on his most select committee that for three or four days Sir Sing-Along Strain enjoyed his chairmanship and needed little support from the clever London Ph.D. Members accepted that throughout the devising and eventual presentation of the new curriculum there should be an understanding on the part of parents and professional tutors that there would be the incorporation of an agreed set of broad social values. This set should underpin all that was done within the curriculum, and while its transmission might appear at times to be incidental, its instillation would be firm, reasoned and ongoing.

The most select committee, readily persuaded by the volume of the corrrespondence it received, agreed that the philosophy underlying the new curriculum should be intelligible to all. Further, they tried to formulate a set of values which most parents already embraced and which many tried to pass on to their children. The values would, if adopted, be ones which aimed to benefit the population as a whole.

The set of values, they decided, would embrace - in random order at this stage - honesty, trust, reliability, industriousness, respect for the legitimate rights of others, tolerance of that which is good, care for weaker members of society, regard for the environment and a kindness towards other people. The select committee hoped that this would lead to a degree of serenity that would make for a happy life. It would incorporate contentment with a lifestyle not dominated by the acquisition of greater and greater personal wealth or by an ever-increasing consumption of diminishing world resources.

"At some point a reversal of this ever-increasing consumption trend has got to be advocated," the liberal lady said. "We might as well start now while the whole education system is being reshaped. That new system can be the means by which such aims are achieved."

No-one argued. Apart from the co-opted members, all present needed to go on record as being firmly in favour of husbanding diminishing world resources.

"This advocacy of an acceptable morality - for that is what we are trying to thrash out here - which will be embodied in the new educational system - is not to be linked to any particular religious doctrine?" asked the pallid mother of seven who, among her other parliamentary duties, represented the nation's parent-governors.

Hurriedly, with anxious glances around the table, the most select committee decided not. As the employers' leader put it, with an attempt at diplomacy, "I foresee trouble when it is known that this is to be a secular doctrine, but I can see even more if it is linked to only one or two faiths and some seem, inadvertently, to have been omitted. I can imagine a hundred times more trouble with that."

So could Sir Sing-Along Strain. Secular it would be.

"No assemblies? No prayers?" asked a conservative member.

"With no schools there will be no assemblies . . ." said the Ph.D.

"No visiting priests, no agnostics taking prayers," said the socialist.

"How charmingly you put things," said the foodstore magnate.

"It is so difficult for us to envisage a society without schools," said the liberal lady, soothingly.

"And, I hope, no national flag fluttering where the headteacher once stood to lead the assembly?" the sceptical socialist continued, unperturbed by animosity. He was thin and lanky. His face had a gaunt look and his heavy spectacles were too large for his nose.

"There will be no school hall in which it or any other flag will flutter. There will be . . ."

". . . no schools and no school halls . . " responded several members of the committee in unison. Over the past few days this had become a frequent refrain and members were amused by the chanting. They all knew it would take time to get used to the idea of a nation without schools and the refrain helped them to adjust.

"And how will these secular values be taught?" It was the disliked lawyer speaking. He did not join the chanting.

To tackle this question, the select committee listed examples of ways in which familes were already passing on successfully such values to their children.

"They are the many families - the vast majority - where there is love for the child and a sense of social responsibility. Where the parent, or parents, or grandparents, believe in the need for such transmission and have some idea of how to do it," offered the parent governor. It was that model, in several versions, that would be the starting point. But now, in addition to family members, the clever Ph.D. pointed out, there would be a professional personal tutor, working with each family and guiding and supporting where she could. Families already teaching at home could receive the same help.

"Help with the transmission?" asked the employers' representative.

"Yes," said the young Ph.D. "And don't let's for a second minimise this challenge to the tutor's work. But, equally, don't let's be defeatist and say, because of perceived problems, we should not aim to incorporate this in the tutor's role. Many families may need help - more than are likely to admit it or accept it at first - but there must be a start."

"We must not underestimate, either, the difficulties there have always been in trying to establish personal relationships and of attempting to instil moral values in classes of thirty pupils or more in schools of a thousand . . . it is no easy task that teachers have now - or did have, I should say." The last speaker was the co-opted ex-secondary school member - an engaging woman of forty-two.

"There were small village schools giving invaluable help in this area . . ." said the parent-governor thoughtfully.

"That was a totally different situation from a school of 2000 . . ." said the lawyer. "The management structure . . ."

"There weren't many of 2000," mumbled somebody else.

There was confusion for a time and Sir Sing-Along lost track of who was saying what and why.

"But it was the little schools that were being closed. And many were doing excellent work. That's the point."

"It's not the point," cried the portly conservative lady, "the point is what do we do now?"

"I trust, Mr Chairman," said the oldest of the ex officio teachers who had retired early from an under funded and over populated technical college in the north, "this committee will make it crystal clear that it is not admonishing the parents and teachers of today - of 1999. I would like it recorded that the committee thinks that most of them have been doing all they can, with limited resources and often against an alien moral background, to promote the very values the committee has been discussing this afternoon."

The speaker was assured that his views were those of the whole committee.

"And will be minuted?" The teacher was a lay-preacher and an ardent supporter of a children's charity which had received much support from several local schools and colleges.

"Yes," said the clever Ph.D., and he nodded to the minuting

secretary as if to confirm the point.

"What we all have to do," the Ph.D. continued, "is convince people who have been working in the now defunct system that what they are being offered are better opportunities to do the same valuable work that they were attempting in the past. That positive approach must be paramount. This committee was not established to be one of enquiry, but to be one of recommendation."

"I fail to see how the second can be done without reference to the first," commented the disliked lawyer, "but have it as you please."

The select committee did. They accepted the Ph.D.'s stipulation and began to examine how they saw the transmission of values taking place.

First, family. This, with its own personal tutor, would become an integral part of the new no-schools system and would encourage the acquisition of these values. Then the counselling skills attained by personal tutors in training and through subsequent experience would become crucial in influencing parents reluctant to accept help. It was anticipated that there would be failures, especially in the early years. But, in many ways, children would bring back to the family ideas and teaching procedures acquired during tutorial sessions with personal tutors and through their supervised reading and allied studies. Also revealed would be ways of working with parents originating from media teaching programmes. Further, the personal tutor would not be on her own, and some of her allies - working quietly behind the scenes - would be powerful indeed.

"So tutors would be helping with the education of parents and brothers and sisters and even grandparents?" asked the pallid parent-governor.

"I don't think I would put it exactly like that - not quite so starkly," demurred the Ph.D. cautiously. "It might give a false impression if put in that way."

"But it would be nothing new. I learned a lot about literature and many other subjects when my children were at school. I enjoyed it. I even took up my French again . . . I welcomed new ideas and fresh input from the teachers," persisted the parent-governor.

"I am sure you did, but it could be unwise, even foolhardy, to suggest at this stage that a major aim of the new approach was to tutor parents . . . "

"But incidentally . . . in a friendly way . . ."

"Maybe. But I am sure it would be better left unsaid and, Mr Chairman, certainly left unminuted?" insisted the percipient Ph.D.

The exchange was not minuted.

The most select committee agreed that the 'good' influences of parents and the wider family would be developed and reinforced by tutors. Personal tutors would need to be aware of each child's background and the influences that affected the learning situation. They would have much to learn from many families.

"Suppose," asked the employers' representative impassively, "she came across cases of child neglect or cruelty? I can see real problems there."

The suave man was not alone. Sir Sing-Along Strain could see them in profusion. He sought guidance.

It came from the co-opted ex-primary school headteacher. She said that while such incidents were rare . . .

"Rare? One is one too many," snapped the socialist.

"I was going to say that they may well become even rarer when we have skilled, caring tutors helping families or groups of families. Help, support and guidance is what such families most often need. But, of course, if she suspects abuse of any kind she must seek assistance from other authorities. She must never take risks."

"And we must stress that their primary role is tutoring, not social work," said the portly conservative adamantly.

"Yes, but social workers will still be needed in many areas."

"Quite so," said Sir Sing-Along, seeking comfort. "Quite so."

There was general assent. Social workers would still be needed.

"And drugs?"

The chairman fidgeted with his agenda. Drugs? These unpleasant areas were alien to him. He was apprehensive again.

"I suggest a similarly cautious approach. But I do feel that the new organisation of teaching which the committee has in mind will, in itself, be a deterrent." It was the same compelling ex-headteacher.

Relief was shown by many members and they returned to the passing on of values. But a few had jotted down 'drugs' and 'abuse' for future debate. They intended to take both matters further.

It then was claimed that a personal tutor would have better opportunities for instilling society's desired values effectively than a schoolteacher had enjoyed in the school-based system. A tutor would be dealing frequently for sustained periods with individual children or small groups and with parents. She would have close and intense contact with each pupil for two years while the child was in her personal group. She would have an ongoing contact for eight years while the child was in her tutor panel. She would be able to devise a personal curriculum for each child based, initially, on literature, drama, art and music. She would have many advantages and enormous responsibility.

"Parents and tutors must not be afraid of controlling the young child's development," said the portly conservative. "In the past, the need for guidelines was not emphasised enough. Nor," she added, "did we, in this select committee, put this item strongly enough in considering 'needs' in our earlier sessions. There has, for years, been an understandable reluctance amongst some teachers and parents to correct a child or even to point him in the right direction."

The tired trades union spokesman made as if to speak, but changed his mind and sat back in his seat. There was a pause.

Then the liberal lady suggested that another need that had been inadequately stressed earlier was that the child had a need 'to be able to tell someone . . . in a way and in a relationship that was simple and matter of fact, about all kinds of things.' Each child needed to be able to talk about his achievements, disappointments, hopes, fears, worries . . . to someone he trusted and respected and whom he knew would listen attentively and respond positively: someone who had the time and the inclination and the professional skills to make, whenever possible, realistic recommendations and responses. There would be times when the personal tutor would be by far the best person to fill this role and times when that work would be the most important work she would ever do. "This need, too," she said, "must be allowed for in the curriculum."

Thirty years later, Susan Smith knew this well. Her professional skills, aided by the arts-based curriculum, had helped many a child with a personal problem and often his family as well. Some three-quarters of her time with pupils was spent on work, formal and informal, which arose from the arts-based syllabus. Well over half of that was from literature - novels, short stories, biographies and autobiographies, plays, poems and legends. That reading and subsequent study became the starting point in much counselling work. The other quarter of her teaching time she devoted to developing skills in numeracy and literacy, and to helping with the development of pupils' general knowledge and other interests.

Although Susan did not know the ins and outs of the most select committee's deliberations, she had heard of difficulties it experienced in putting through the largely literature-based model. Some parents and ex-teachers had not, at first, seen the full potential of teaching through literature. But good work done in pilot areas by enthusiasts with the help of excellent programmes from the National Media Library - on which money had been lavished - won many converts. It was now accepted by the bulk of the population that education was synonymous with literature just as it had once been regarded as synonymous with school-based teaching in crowded classrooms.

Susan Smith approved heartily of the select committee's recommendations of three decades ago. Her initial tutor-training course and her five years' tutoring experience had proved the value of literature as the core subject. The benefits arising from what she and her pupils read together went far beyond tutorial room, study or library and they remained for life.

With her tutor panel colleagues she accepted that from the young child through to college leaver and beyond, literature had most to offer in the inculcation of the values desired by society and set out by the most select committee in 1999. A skilful, careful, gentle approach in considering all that was read with children and a period of patient waiting while ideas germinated did much to achieve the desired social and moral ends and to affect the cultural mores.

But, of even greater importance as far as the welfare of the individual child was concerned, was that the reading helped greatly when personal problems were met. The discussion of shyness with a shy child was made natural and effective when it led from the shyness and painful reserve of a character in a skilfully written story and was interpreted at a level of understanding appropriate to the intellectual and emotional stage of the child. So, too, with family problems: the 'fiction' chosen for study was the very cornerstone of initial ice-breaking discussions. The same had been true of sexual and other delicate issues.

There had been times, as some committee members had forecast, when such work proved to be far more important than the mere mechanics of literacy and numeracy or anything else. Susan had read the committee's 1999 report while at university, for it had become an even greater landmark in the history of educational development than the Acts of 1870, 1902 or 1918, or even that much hailed 1944 Education Act with its school-based reorganisation and extension. But much of the late 20th Century discussion in Sir Sing-Along's committee she had not read, nor had her professors, for it had not been minuted. As the bright young Ph.D. had said at the time, "People will begin worrying all over again if we suggest that there will be times when even literacy and numeracy take a back seat while literature drives the bus."

Where the young academic had been inaccurate was in his forecasting of how often the old 'basic subjects' would take second place. For Susan and her charges these times were many. There were frequent occasions when helping with personal problems and the uncertainties of childhood and adolescence took precedence over all else. Seeing the definition of 'curriculum' in this wider sense, Susan knew that this sympathetic help with social and psychological development had become the crux of that curriculum.

Susan's ability to give additional emphasis to music and art helped even further with the task of encouraging children to study their own culture - a word used by Susan and her colleagues to mean the whole way of life of a people. They looked at their own lives, the lives of others in their society, and saw how frequently they affected each other. Children were enabled to see that very little that they did had no consequences at all for other people.

Susan Smith's professional inheritance from the deliberations of Sir Sing-Along's most select committee was, after two or three decades, taken for granted and firmly established. There had been no counter-movement to return the nation to school-based teaching. With the success achieved by the implementation of personal study programmes and their acceptance by parents, this now seemed unlikely. The only threat was that the 'new' system would be challenged by something even more radical than that which had emerged in 1999. But whatever that was, and whatever technology would make possible in 2099 or 2199, the societal need for developing deep personal relationships between child, family and tutor would be essential: in fact the greater the technological innovation, the more the personal, human element in education would need to be sustained.

The inheritance of being able to teach via the medium of literature was a highly prized one. The criticisms raised about this after Sir Sing-Along's select committee published its report had not been resurrected. There were no longer cries that literature was being 'used' or 'misused' by being made the nub of the new curriculum, or that it was being debased as a tool of the sociologists, criminologists, social psychologists and social anthropologists. The men and women compiling guidelines for the new generation of personal tutors had been sensitive of such criticism and had ensured that literature stood in its own right as 'the subject of all subjects'. Personal tutors, in everyone's interests - including their pupils', their own and those of the literary purists - ensured that the books, plays and poems read and studied were, above all, enjoyable, stimulating and rewarding works in themselves and that they were seen as such. Their inherent possibilities for thought, ideas and discussion were to be limited only by the ability of the tutor, parent and pupil fully to appreciate them. The books all sat waiting to be enjoyed at a variety of levels. So did the music and art that sat with them in every child's study programme.

"If children, often with parents, met their tutors only two or three times a week and read stories together and discussed the ideas arising from them and were then enabled to see the relevance to their own lives of much that was read, and if, together, they discussed those ideas - and did little else - wouldn't that be enough?"

This had been ventured by a student in Susan's university seminar group of 2022.

"Would very much else matter?" he had asked. "By having those few hours with their tutor each week, in tiny groups, reading great literature, wouldn't that be better than the years of 'full-time' schooling they were getting under the old system? Far, far better?"

The leading lecturer had had much sympathy with this and so had other students. But she had played safe and said that, fine as it may sound, such an approach might be seen as 'too narrow'. It would take a long time for ideas like that to be fully absorbed. Her view was, reluctantly, accepted.

Susan is aware now, in 2029, of the benefits of organising the bulk of her teaching around literature. All of them are additional to, or incidental to, the sheer enjoyment of what is read. Much of her professional work with children in history, geography, art and music and science originates in those novels, biographies, autobiographies and media library programmes which feature the lives and work of eminent people from many walks of life.

She always makes sure that the books she encourages her pupils to read, by themselves or with her or with parents, possess an absorbing story which, by itself, holds the interest of the reader and provides enjoyment. But the reading also involves children in the ongoing process of seeing how their world has come to be as it is and what forces or influences might change it for good or ill. Susan always tries to ensure, treading delicately as she does so, that these benefits emerge.

To Susan Smith and her colleagues working in 2029 it has

become an essential part of the whole educative process that children understand the reasons for their own and other people's patterns of behaviour. They give literature and its associated studies - and the work that develops from them - vital parts to play in the development of that understanding.

But this whole area, on which Susan spent much study time during her preparation for tutorship at university, is still one requiring careful handling. Never does she permit literature to become subservient to geography or history or the sciences or any of the 'old' subjects. Nor does she let it become merely a means of convenient illustration. But she does allow it, even encourages it, to cross 'subject boundaries' - boundaries which were, she was told, arbitrarily determined frontiers in the school-based system. Susan knows that the extensive reading she undertakes with her pupils helps them understand the whole human condition. For instance the reading of a children's story which, incidentally, indicated how climate or terrain or an invention or discovery affected or shaped a culture might begin a scheme of work on social, anthropological, historical, biological and other aspects of that country or region. But the introduction of excerpts from that book, seeming to the child to be incidental, may be instrumental in encouraging the reading of the complete novel by children who may not, working in a more rigidly compartmentalised timetable, be prompted so to read. Indeed, she had been told that in a separate-subject curriculum, those children could be suspicious of the same novel's introduction by a teacher of English literature who had to see the title in terms of a set book or part of a distantly ordained syllabus. They might give it a cooler reception.

But literature does not dominate all Susan Smith's work. In compiling each child's study programme, she ensures adequate time is allowed for progress in literacy and numeracy. While development of the former is inevitably related to work in literary studies, the acquisition of specific listening, speaking, reading and writing skills is carefully assessed. Deficiencies are corrected. Similarly, but more exactly, number concepts and skills are thoughtfully taught. Children's learning here, as elsewhere, is aided greatly by expert teaching from the National Media Library where a wide choice of graded, interesting work can be introduced and explained by skilled practitioners, and reinforced at home by parents.

In both these key areas, literacy and numeracy, Susan is able to use methods and select content appropriate to the needs of each pupil. She can examine, diagnose, treat, reassess, revise and record. She must, as an essential part of her professionalism, know what help is available from colleagues, resource centres, the NML, and other sources. She can make use of them and explain to parents what she is doing. There is some similarity with the work of family doctors, particularly with their work in promoting good health rather than in treating existing illness. And the similarity between doctor and tutor extends to professional recognition in society.

Although she does not, as yet, appreciate it fully, Susan is helped by the whole milieu in which her work takes place. There is increased help from parents and, as early retirement becomes commonplace, from grandparents too. There is help available to her tutor panel from consultants, for which the panel pays, and also from staff and facilities at community resource centres and from the NML. Frequent formal and informal meetings with the child's family members help, as do Susan's own keenly developed skills of observation and assessment which enable her to identify social or academic problems at an early stage.

In the fourth broad area of the curriculum prescribed by Sir Sing-Along's select committee, Susan enjoys much success. She encourages her pupils to develop existing interests and introduces them to new ones. Many of these, she hopes, will prove to be of long-term benefit.

With her colleagues, Susan was taught, in her course of professional preparation, to notice interests of pupils as revealed by themselves and as reported by their families and friends and by her own surveillance.

With children of the age group she teaches, the emphasis of Susan's work in this area is on the introduction of children to new ideas and experiences. This is done by means of visits, topic work, reading, films, video recordings, media programmes, plays, talks, demonstrations and through the activities and interests of parents and of other tutors and students in the tutor panel and at the community resource centre.

Where an emerging interest emanates from what used to be regarded as a traditional subject area, Susan encourages this. In the same way, by using facilities at the community resource centre, she promotes keenness in sports and persuades pupils - often with the help of resource centre staff more experienced and proficient than she - to take up a variety of sporting activities.

Already Susan's pupils are competent with basic computer

technology and its practical uses. Many who want to take their studies beyond the solely utilitarian will be enabled to do so. Spectacular work is being done with two pupils by a parent who works in conjunction with a staff member at the local resource centre. The same parent, a programming expert, has helped more than twenty pupils from tutor panel groups over the past six years. In another area, two children who left Susan's group four years ago have been helping with film and video making in conjunction with work being prepared by their tutors. A father and an aunt are helping here. One has already decided that the 'interest' could turn into a career, but he is encouraged to leave his options open.

Following their reading, programme study, educational visits and other stimulants, many children in Susan's tutor panel are showing interest in unusual pursuits. At present these include collecting old bottles, handbell ringing, spiders, Roman coins, Irish folklore, canal locks, gibbons of the Malay peninsula, the origins of rugby football, fifes, insects attracted to English garden pinks, pioneer aviators, early Antarctic expeditions and the salvaging of famous wrecks.

But beyond all this, beyond the literature which Susan and her pupils enjoy, beyond the literacy, numeracy and general knowledge the pupils need to have, beyond the desire to know how things work and where things come from, beyond the personal interests which are slowly developing and being explored, beyond all these are important aspects of the curriculum hidden from normal view. These concealed aspects, while they often arise from other work, are sometimes of greater significance to the child and his tutor than all the other parts of the curriculum added together.

These are the myriad subtle ways in which a skilled, sensitive and appreciative tutor in close contact with the pupil and his family and friends can help with the range of issues that can be distressing to children and adolescents and give them problems in adjusting to a widening and often perplexing environment. Problems of diffidence and self-consciousness, worries about relationships with the opposite sex, loneliness and 'not being wanted', anxiety about difficulties in the family, concern about appearance, about apparent inadequacies in academic work or sport, of 'not being liked by other people', about irrational fears, dread of being ridiculed; all are of a significance to the young person that can far outweigh the importance of a grade in English or a mark gained in mathematics.

Help can be given in these areas through the adroitness of a personal tutor who knows her pupils well. The expertise in dealing with human relationships born of training and experience can often with a word, a glance, a shrug of the shoulders or a smile, relieve a tension that has been present for days or weeks or months: a tension that has undermined other work the young person has been required to do or interests he has wanted to follow. Without the relief of that tension much else that a tutor tries to do will be partly - even wholly - irrelevant. The parent is sometimes too close, too concerned, too anxious to know what to do for the best - even if he or she has the necessary time, skills and experience to try to solve the problem alone.

The most select committee members had, in 1999, considered this matter at length. It had troubled them all. One ex-teacher had worried Sir Sing-Along by insisting that some of her colleagues in the schools had been under such stress themselves that their need of counselling was as great as that of their charges. Often, she had emphasised, they were not in a position to give quiet, long-term ministering to a worried child no matter how much they longed to do so. Sir Sing-Along and several other committee members seemed genuinely astounded at this.

"It is quite true," one of the other ex-teachers confirmed, "but I must say, too, that some teachers did not see such ministering as part of their role and others did not have the time or energy to take it on. They had a National Curriculum to wade through, tests to administer, grades to award and scores to record, important meetings to attend, vital forms to fill in, appraisal to prepare for, frustration to overcome and weariness to conquer. Not only did they not have the time, energy or skills often needed to cope adequately with John's problems with his single parent mother and her new partner, but they did not, for a long time, even know about them. If they had known . . . if they had had time . . . if they had had the skills . . . so many 'ifs', so little done." He had been as angry as he was sad. No one else on the most select committee had spoken for almost a minute. Some members had stared in disbelief.

Many of the weaknesses of the school-based system had been revealed to Susan in her training and in her general reading. Instances had been quoted by her professors who had, themselves, been exposed to the system as pupils and teachers.

"You see," one had expounded, "reaching set standards in this or that was vital to both teacher and child. That was what politicians demanded. Thoughtful, concerned teachers who had wrestled with the demands of pastoral care for years, realised with great regret that Andrew's understanding of why steam lifted the kettle's lid seemed to be more important than recognising why his father was persistently angry and rapidly destroying the family's happiness and Andrew's self-confidence. It's unbelievable now, isn't it?"

To Susan Smith and fellow students it was. They were pleased that education had moved on to involve so closely child, parent and tutor.

Sir Sing-Along Strain would have been pleased, too, if, some years after his select committee's lengthy deliberations, he could have seen the great good it had done. But the knight had moved on, too. He had died long before the beneficial effect of that work had made itself apparent to the nation. His career, after his death, merited only four lines in most dictionaries of biography.

Even his chairmanship of the select committee was not immediately included in official papers, but was noted briefly in an obituary in *The Guardian* newspaper of the time. The full significance of the committee's work was not generally grasped until ten years after Sir Sing-Along's death. Then it was dealt with in full by a burrowing researcher who compiled and published at the timeliest of moments a 300-page illustrated biography of *Sir Sing-Along Strain, Statesman.* The book appeared in twenty-three languages, was serialised in a Sunday newspaper, made into a notable film, and enabled the author to retire on her royalties at the tender age of thirty-two.

A Wealthy Foodstore Magnate

Whenever Susan Smith, sitting comfortably at home, faxed her computerised grocery order to the local depot of Bigga Storr Foods Ltd., she knew that if it was not delivered to her apartment within sixty minutes she would receive the order free of charge. But she did not know that such slick, no-errors-ever-made organisation was the work of the very same woman who had masterminded the professional way of working Susan now enjoyed.

One of Bigga Storr Foods' dominating directors and outstanding planners of the mid-1990s had been a wealthy, determined, resourceful and forward-looking businesswoman. She had been drafted, ex officio, onto Sir Sing-Along Strain's most select committee and it was she who had both established and fine-tuned the nationwide home-based personal tutoring scheme, supportive panels, resource centres and National Media Library.

By 1999 this self-made multi-millionaire and magnate of the food trade had become a leading public figure. Known for her ability to organise on the grand scale, she had been consulted frequently by politicians anxious to economise. Leading educational administrators, keen to get something right, had whispered her name to Sir Sing-Along Strain and enrolled she had been. It was clear that her prowess at easing two million sardines through two thousand food outlets every week was exactly what was needed for the smooth redeployment of the country's four hundred thousand teachers.

To Sir Sing-Along's undisguised relief, the food-store magnate agreed to chair an organisational sub-committee to report back on the practicalities of reorganisation.

"But we are not reorganising the system," cried the sceptical socialist indignantly. "We've done with that. We've all had a bellyful of reorganising over the past forty years. Forget it !"

"Maybe, maybe," said Sir Sing-Along with some irritation, "but someone has to organise something. Someone has to decide where seven million children go, with whom, where, when and for how long. Surely you see that?"

A sub-committee was the answer. It was always sound policy when things got tricky. It removed pressure from the chairman and delayed delectably delicate decisions. It was with great pleasure, therefore, that the artful knight watched the foodstore magnate stride purposefully into an inner room, taking with her six members of his committee. She was the sort of bossy, forever-organising, thrusting woman he could not abide: the very stuff of his nightmares. He watched her departure, gave thanks for his bachelorhood, and prepared to leave for the sanctuary of his nearby club.

"How many pupils will each tutor have?" the foodstore director asked, getting down to business straight away.

"Fifteen," said the ex-primary school headteacher and co-opted member.

Twenty was agreed, for the chairlady soon calculated that setting the group size at fifteen would cause them to go wildly over budget. Her remit was not to exceed by more than five per cent the current costs of education. A saving of five per cent might bring her a knighthood - or whatever it was that a lady tycoon might earn for such valued public service.

So it was decided that, after a three month period of preparation and retraining, all those teachers currently in service who wished to tutor children would be given full professional responsibility for a group of twenty pupils. During the teachers' period of intensive retraining most schools would be closed and a dismantling of their heavy equipment would begin prior to their sale or demolition.

To pay for the new system, central government would calculate the cost of teaching one pupil in the old system and would then, after deducting ten per cent to pay for support services and resources and the very minimum of administration, allocate that sum to each tutor each year for each pupil in the tutor's personal group. The foodstore magnate ruled out local education authorities' participation since she felt that would add unnecessarily to the costs. She was a cost-conscious woman. She asked the sub-committee to agree to the money being paid directly to tutors quarterly in advance, as she remembered only too painfully the cash flow problems she had experienced in her early trading years.

The clever Ph.D. smiled behind his hand. "Personal accountability already? I thought we'd soon get onto that . . ."

It was ruled that each personal tutor would be associated with five colleagues. That small group of six, all of whom would live in the same locality, would form the basic working and administrative unit of the new, non-school system. The group would be known as a tutor panel and would be as vital to the new system of education as each child's family would be to the wider community in which the system would operate.

Such an arrangement would permit each pupil to be tutored by five people: one to each of the five two-year periods that would make up the decade of early education from four to thirteen years. These five tutors, plus the sixth, would form one team or panel or practice, which in its turn would be linked to a resource centre.

"Why is a sixth tutor needed?" asked the disliked lawyer.

The portly conservative member of parliament had been about to ask the same question.

"It is an extravagance," she glowered.

"That will be made quite clear shortly," said the co-opted ex-headteacher who had pressed for the inclusion. "Her duties will be specific and beneficial. Don't worry, she'll earn her keep."

The same member explained that each tutor panel would meet the broad educational needs of some one hundred pupils, drawn from approximately fifty families. The panel would be largely self-sufficient in terms of tutoring skills, the meeting of curriculum requirements and the financing, regulation and administration of its work.

Parents, it was noted, would choose a tutor panel for their child well before his fourth birthday and that panel would be responsible for his wellbeing for the next ten years.

"But only if he stays with that tutor panel," prompted the pallid parent governor. "He doesn't have to?"

"No. His parents can switch panels for him."

"Will the same tutor in the panel always tutor the same age group - say the four and five year olds?" asked the lawyer, deliberately.

"Usually," said the London Ph.D., butting in. He knew the question had been asked because there had been disagreement earlier. "We think most tutors would wish to specialise in one age group - especially to begin with."

"But if this new educational technology turns out to be all it's cracked up to be," insisted the sceptical socialist, "it should be possible for any tutor within a panel to have a personal group of pupils of mixed ages and still devise an individual study programme for each. That could make her work more interesting and give greater flexibility regarding the time she keeps a pupil - she might keep him for five years or eight or the whole ten if that's what she and the parents want and can show it's best for the child."

But the philosophy that the personal tutor should get to know well and become proficient in tutoring one two-year age group won the day. The foodstore magnate was a firm believer in specialism whether in cheeses, meats, fruits, fish or anything else. It paid off handsomely in her business and would do elsewhere: and she was a most persuasive lady.

"It need not be fixed for ever," submitted the London Ph.D. "And it would help greatly in the organising of social events and with the development of friendships if children in the tutor groups were of a similar age." He paused. "It could be varied, perhaps experimentally, within tutor panels?"

The foodstore magnate thought not. She favoured clear and careful labelling of everything. Two-year tutoring, of a specified age group, by specified tutors, was agreed to. But there was muttering.

"What about this sixth tutor? It still seems an extravagance," complained the conservative lady.

It was pointed out that the additional tutor would, for a period of two years, have no personal group of students. Approved and designated by her colleagues, she would act as chairperson to the panel for that time, then she would resume her equally important role of personal tutor and be replaced as chairperson by another elected colleague.

The chairperson would have many responsibilities. These would include helping with tutoring in colleagues' groups as required, helping pupils who had particular learning difficulties, meeting the needs of the exceptionally able, engaging in research and private study, aiding probationer entrants to the new profession, helping with the preparation and assessment of new teaching aids, suggesting alternatives or fresh ideas, coping with sickness and maternity and paternity leave . . ."

"So tutors will be allowed babies?" asked the sceptical socialist mockingly.

"Of course. Why ever not?" snapped the foodstore magnate.

"Well, within my lifetime women teachers had to pack in the job if they as much as got married, let alone had kids," he retorted.

"And the factory workers did a fourteen-hour day. But it's not relevant!" barked the conservative. "Let's deal with the future, shall we? Your kind always have to drag up the past and everything that was bad about it."

"Temper, temper," said the socialist. "One up to me," he thought, gleefully. He loathed the portly conservative and all she stood for.

But the foodstore magnate pressed on. She explained that, with other tutors, the chairperson would arrange for the interviewing and appointment of tutors to the panel, and of staff for the community resource centre. She would be able to release panel tutors for study leave, at home or abroad, on a regular basis; the initial target would be the equivalent of six months' study leave for each ten years of service.

"An excellent facility which has been disgracefully lacking in the past," offered the co-opted ex-headteacher.

No comment was made by fellow sub-committee members. Their own jobs had not given them that facility, either, and they were not convinced of its necessity...

They next heard that a major task of the panel chairperson would be to see that the panel maintained a balance of tutoring skills appropriate to the tutoring of children in the four to thirteen age range. Working with the children's parents, the panel would be deeply involved in the social and educational development of one hundred young people. Within that ten year age span, the hundred children would have a wide range of aptitude and ability, so most tutors would decide - certainly initially - to concentrate on tutoring one or two of the early education stages. However each tutor would be expected to contribute to the academic and recreational activities of the panel as a whole and to offer an expertise in several tutoring areas of her own choosing. Also, as opportunities arose, each tutor would give general advice across the five age groups.

"When are we coming to the statutory protection of children? What will be the legal requirements placed on panel chairpersons and tutors regarding the care of children? What will be their obligations in law?" The lawyer rapped out his questions.

"Here we go," murmured the sceptical and somewhat weary socialist. "Jobs for the boys in curly wigs..."

"Obligations in law, sir. I take it you have no objection to our children being protected by law?"

"How do they need protecting? And who from? Aren't tutors to be trusted? Aren't parents to be trusted? Don't you lot trust anyone?"

"It is not a matter of trust - certainly not of trust alone. There have to be clearly defined areas of responsibility, and legal redress for negligence. And there is the whole minefield of contracts..."

"Should we start with the areas of responsibility?" suggested the foodstore magnate. She had enough of contracts in her business.

"Very well. It must be made crystal clear that tutor and parent share responsibility in law for the child's protection... especially if this scheme is to start with children as young as four. To begin with, and as we hear so much about the tutor being a professional person, I propose the onus be on her to keep an agreed logbook detailing each child's movements and activities for each forthcoming week, and that a copy be lodged, against a signature, with parent or guardian. The log would serve as a work-forecast and would show where the child is supposed to be, when, with whom, and for how long."

"I think that's very important," said the parent-governor. "And we need to know who is taking each child to and from ..."

"Thank you," said the disliked lawyer. "That is my second point. Certainly until the child is seven he or she must be accompanied by a responsible adult ..."

"Arranging all that would be such a bonus . . ." suggested the parent-governor. "Agreeing times and places and escorts and pupil companions ... and I would go beyond seven for this care and ..."

"All reasonable care given the particular circumstances of the occasion," interrupted the lawyer. "An essential continuation of the *in loco parentis* precedents ..."

"Come off it, pal. You're talking about the plain, straightforward common sense that parents and teachers have been using for a hundred years. Pity we don't have a bit more of that in the law!"

The contempt in the socialist's voice for this representative of the law and for the law in general was clear to all. The London Ph.D., although no fan of the lawyer himself, felt deeply uncomfortable at the socialist's gibing. Could this man not see that it was politicians who made the law, not lawyers?

"Ninety-nine per cent of tutors and parents will see to this without the law's intrusion," explained the disliked lawyer contemptuously. He was far too practised to be drawn by such transparent goading. "We need simply to ensure by means of the law that there is full compliance, especially in the administration of a scheme that could well be fraught with legal hazards ..."

"And fat fees."

"I resent that, Madam Chairman, I really do!"

"*Madam Chairman*" teased the socialist, scenting blood. "Don't you know what sex she is? Or how to address the Chair?"

"I trust the member ..."

"I think the sub-committee will recommend a detailed future log be carefully kept by each tutor for each child in her personal group," said the foodstore magnate. "It would become part of her weekly planning of the learning programme for her pupils - on which prog- ramming we are already agreed."

The chairperson defused the situation further by calling for a show of hands. The proposal was carried. The disliked lawyer had won not only the vote but the increased respect of the chairperson and the clever Ph.D.

"You mentioned a bonus?" said the chairperson to the pallid parent-governor.

"Yes. If this 'whereabouts' log is to be required of all by law - as has rightly been insisted - then it will provide immediate and inescapable points of contact between personal tutor and parent, especially with a parent who is reluctant to talk, for whatever reason, to a tutor during the early years."

"That's all very well," said the socialist. He was feeling angry at being bettered, but he was always upset by the very presence of the public school and ancient university law school member: they had clashed on previous occasions. "What about families where both parents - or perhaps single parents - have to go out to work to make ends meet? Who's going to look after the children? They need the schools or something like them. They need to know where the kids are. They want them looked after for the day, not fobbed off with your 'inescapable points of contact'."

He bit his tongue. He had said too much. That last sentence would be grist to the mill for his opponents. But there was silence. No one took him up on his remark. No one pressed him on whether he, or some parents, had seen the schools' primary function as being one of childminding. They were letting him off the hook: they were taking him seriously! He noticed the disliked lawyer penning notes.

"I have tentative figures, Madam Chairman," came from the clever Ph.D. He was nervous. He had felt impelled to break the silence. "They might reassure members."

The chairperson nodded. The sub-committee of the most select committee stared at him expectantly. The young academic elab- orated:

"The personal tutor would, over a year, be wholly and profes- sionally engaged in fulfilling her contractual duties for . . ."

"You mean, she'd work?" asked the sceptical socialist, bluntly.

"She'd work for 35 - 45 hours a week, arranging the times herself. She would arrange days off, study periods and holidays after consultation with parents, colleagues and older pupils. She would be in direct tutoring contact with each pupil for some seven hours per week assuming she tutored them, on average, in groups of four or five."

"Seven hours?" scoffed the socialist. "Only seven hours?"

The pallid parent-governor and mother of seven - five still at home - looked worried.

"Then there would be some five or six hours per week during which the child - particularly the very young child - would be supervised in activities at the community resource centre. There would be, too, for those parents who chose to use it, six or seven hours per week available for young children at official childcare centres run by local authorities or other agencies for which the parent would pay the economic cost out of enhanced child benefit allowances."

"Pay!" cried the sceptical socialist. But the Ph.D. ploughed on:

"Finally, but of great importance, the parent would supervise pre-set studies arranged with the personal tutor linked to the lesson output of the National Media Library: that would be for ten to twelve hours although some parents would spend far more time on the work and its associated activities. But I stress this is an estimate. All the figures are provisional. They come to some twenty-five hours a week. But nothing is fixed. The sub-committee has to decide what recommendations it will make."

"It will be a target?" asked the conservative lady, quietly.

"More of a guideline," the Ph.D. replied. "In a week when children are away on residential study visits it could be seventy hours. At other times, with sickness, holidays - it could be none at all."

"None? Parents would soon want the schools back," rasped the sceptical socialist.

"You have to remember," countered the Ph.D. almost aggressively, "that parents have done without the schools for ten or twelve weeks every year for decades past: *and* in the evenings *and* at weekends *and* when their children have been ill. They have been managing. Some parents actually like having their children around!"

It was the Ph.D.'s turn to regret a remark, but the socialist member had upset him with what seemed to be manifestations of the most reactionary attitudes: yet the same man would claim to have a predominantly progressive outlook on life. Now the parent-governor smiled. She was pleased to see the young man had virility.

"You're quite right," she said. "They do! And they will do under the new system, for under that they will be getting ongoing help all through the year. Most parents will be much better off ..."

"And so will the children . . ." said the Ph.D. in the lowest of low voices. "So will the children . . ."

The portly conservative lady smiled: she had heard him.

"This young fellow will go far," she thought. "Quite far unless I'm much mistaken."

She was not much mistaken. The Ph.D. became, in April 2018, Minister for Education in the first government to be formed by The Progressive People's Party for Universal Peace and Tranquillity. Who could go further than that?

But there was more work to be done. The sub-committee of the most select committee of 1999 moved on to consider the disliked lawyer's next point: the need - in law - for tutor panels regularly to produce and publish brochures describing their work.

"The brochure would give parents vital information as of right . . ."

"A legal right?" queried the parent governor. The Ph.D. smiled.

". . . a legal right. Contractual documentation readily available."

Although she often grew tired of them, the food store magnate appreciated the importance of contracts as many were made for her company's benefit every week. It was agreed, after some de-debate, that panel brochures should be obligatory.

"They will be helpful to parents and give tutors a peg on which to hang their gowns," the conservative member assented.

"Gowns? And mortar boards? And fur-lined hoods?" snarled the sceptical socialist. But he was ignored.

"No sense of tradition," murmured the ex-headteacher sadly as the committee moved on.

They were told that the brochure would give information about the panel's structure and its work. It would be revised every two years by each incoming chairperson. It would set out the membership of the panel, giving tutors' names, addresses, qualifications, tutoring and other experience and curriculum and leisure interests. It would give brief examples of earlier individual study programmes prepared for pupils in order to illustrate the curriculum range offered and the principal ways of working.

The brochure would be freely available from the chairperson or any tutor, or from a local community resource centre, town hall or public library. The basic information would be available on screen in any resource centre or parental study room via the National Media Library.

The sub-committee's intention was that by careful comparison of brochures and discussion of them with panel chairpersons, parents would have considerable knowledge of the tutor panels available before they had to place their children. Panels would rely for pupil-recruitment on their reputations for sound, caring tutoring and on the quality of the relationships they had established with other parents and their children.

The disliked lawyer gained the food store magnate's support as the sub-committee's work progressed. He was able to have written into the final report the rule that no funds would be available to any panel which consistently failed to recruit pupils. However, there would be a breathing space to enable the Professional Tutors' Guild (PTG) to help such panels with advice before recruitment reached dangerously low levels. The PTG would, on request, provide a team of experienced panel chairpersons from other areas to examine and recommend.

The co-opted ex-teacher member said it was important that the brochure should help tutors who wished to move to take up work with another tutor-panel. The brochure data should cover seven main fields. Tutors, like parents, should be able to compare panels before deciding to submit an application to any one. The latest information about any panel nationwide, updated weekly, would be available on screen through the National Media Library (NML).

Then, after some wrangling, the sub-committee agreed to the inclusion of seven main sections in each brochure. Most of these were included at the behest of the disliked lawyer.

The first would contain professional details of tutors. These would include university attended, subjects read, degree obtained, age groups of children preferred for tutoring, subjects and topics emphasised, leisure interests, tutoring experience and a recent photograph. There were objections to the photograph from less photogenic sub-committee members who empathised with tutors, but these were overruled by the chairperson, who considered her own features perfectly presentable. Tutors would be photographed.

The second part would be a statement of each tutor's aims and her order of priorities regarding major areas of the curriculum. Not only would this provide information for parents but it would prompt tutors periodically to clarify their thoughts.

"That is good," said the conservative member, "although two years seems a long time between thoughts."

Surprisingly, for he normally disagreed with everything a conservative said on principle, the sceptical socialist nodded approval.

"Teachers in the old system quite frequently reviewed their philosophies, although they were given precious little time in which to do so because of the demands of politicians," retorted the ex-headteacher. "Tutors in the new system will have the time and the incentive to review what they are doing."

But she was finding less sympathy for teachers' causes on this sub-committee than she had found in the full body. She suspected membership had been loaded against teachers. But the sub-committee, under the the foodstore magnate, moved on.

The third part of the brochure would be a schedule of times and places for parent-tutor consultations. These would normally be in the tutor's own home or in pupils' homes. Despite the doubts of the professor from Alabama, a start was to be made on the provision of study rooms in a sample of new houses, and trials begun on conversions in old ones. Where existing accommodation was quite inadequate, small study rooms would be available temporarily in resource centres. The ex-teacher member disliked this plan, as she wanted relationships to be informal and such scheduling suggested formality. But the disliked lawyer squashed her objections and said that if tutors aspired to the standing of his own profession they must be available at publicised times. His will won.

Secretly, the London Ph.D was pleased. The sometimes notorious 'parents' evenings' of the old school-based system, often hurried, crowded, frantic (even frenetic) and occasionally embarrassingly public, would disappear. What a blessing that would be! But in addition, he heard with less enthusiasm, the panel chairperson would ensure that one tutor would be 'on call' for anxious parents or pupils: she would maintain a rota and include herself on it.

In the fourth part of the panel brochure, extracts would be given from five or so individual study programmes compiled by tutors for pupils of average ability over the ten-year age range of early education. These would give parents an insight into work done and standards expected. They would, too, help stimulate questions from parents and help parents decide how far the objectives of the panel would meet the needs of their children and whether any necessary modifications would be possible.

Then the brochure would show how a panel's work fitted into the wider educational system. It would contain, in common with all published brochures, a rationale for the new personalised curriculum and the guidelines issued to tutors. It would indicate regularly-revised standards of competence in literacy and number work. It would list those of the panel's optional studies likely to be available in middle and later education - the two stages, covering the ages fourteen to sixteen and sixteen to eighteen, with which the tutor panel would be linked.

In the sixth section the brochure would tabulate staff and facilities available to pupils, parents and tutors at the community resource centre to which the panel was affiliated.

"Remember that the resource centres are to be dealt with in another part of the committee's report," said the foodstore magnate. A thorough examination would be made of plans for these centres.

Then, lastly, an agreed national code covering the rights and responsibilities of pupils, parents, tutors and government would be described and explained. The disliked lawyer had been prominent in the code's compilation and was due to present his work to the committee at a later stage. Basically, education would be seen as a voluntary partnership between tutors, parents and pupils based on confidence and co-operation regardless of the existence of national codes. But the code would have legal enforcement. There had been fierce argument about this. The ex-teacher member had wanted it left as a code to be followed voluntarily, but had been defeated by the cogent arguments of the disliked lawyer and the contractually-minded foodstore magnate. However the ex-teacher knew that this point had to go back to the most select committee and that it might be changed. Such was not to be: the legal framework within which the code would work would remain intact. But the disliked lawyer, conversant with possible pitfalls, asked that a no-blame compensation clause be inserted which would protect tutors from fear of being sued for damages in the course of their professional work. The ex-teacher then viewed him more kindly.

The foodstore magnate estimated that, within the designated budget, money could be found to employ a team of computer operators whose task would be to ensure that vacancies for tutors or pupils within each tutor panel were listed as soon as they occurred. Such listings would be available to any parent or tutor throughout the country. At each community resource centre one staff member would have responsibility for ensuring that parents were aware of vacancies. Area print-outs would be available.

Parents would be able to see immediately which panels practised within easy reach of their homes and what vacancies existed. Even more important, forecasts of future vacancies would be available for parents' forward planning. The staff member would, with this data, be able to help parents make the best choice regarding each tutor's age group, sex, marital status, background interests, tutoring topic preferences, favoured tutoring methods, tutoring experience and general educational philosophy. Included in the information, or readily available as an addition to it, would be a list of children being tutored or who had recently been tutored, so that prospective parents could - with the permission of those on the list - approach other parents regarding their opinions of the panel.

"Some tutors and panels will be more popular than others?"

"Yes, just as some doctors and dentists are in more demand than others. Parents must do their homework and register early."

"How much will all this cost?" queried the portly conservative.

"A fraction of a penny per parent spread over the whole country."

"How many will use it? How many will go to all that trouble?"

"Many," butted in the parent governor representative. She was annoyed by what she saw as a slur on parents as a group. "And when it is pointed out to the others that they spend a good deal of time selecting a car to drive, then they can at least spend as much time in choosing a tutor and tutor-panel for their children."

She expected support from the co-opted ex-teacher, but this lady was quiet. She had been silent through most of these recent sessions. Such a detailed brochure, laying down so specifically what was to be done and not done, and what was expected when and where, did not please her. She could see that the disliked lawyer had made an effort to be accommodating to several members of the sub-committee and that, together with his - in her view - unholy alliance with the foodstore magnate, had won points in important areas. She wished the liberal lady had been drafted onto the sub-committee instead of the disliked lawyer. The ex-headteacher feared rigging behind the scenes but could prove nothing. When deliberations returned to the select committee in full session she, and those of her persuasion, would have to ensure that the new system was professional, personal, flexible and within the control of caring tutors working closely with parents. That, after all, was what was expected of the new teaching-without-schools scenario and the new era in which it was to work.

"This new era . . ." said the conservative member as if by telepathy. "This new era will bring different work patterns, duties and roles for parents, won't it? And much higher expectations?"

"Yes," said the chairperson. "Of course."

"Well," continued the portly member, "can we go back to a matter our legal colleague raised so rightly earlier on, the amount of supervision of children there will be. Many parents will soon be in work-share schemes, trying to make the available work go round more equitably. Perhaps many of them will be working only half a week or so - technology will make sure of that. But what a wonderful chance that will offer for parents to join wholeheartedly in the education of their children! Parents will come right back into the picture! Just as the old schools parted parents from their children in the nineteenth century, our new tutoring system will re-unite them in the twenty-first. Whole families will come together to learn. Values will be restored..."

"We are committed to full employment," said the sceptical socialist doggedly. "Your party too, remember."

"So we are all honour-bound to find offices and shops and factories for everyone for evermore, are we?"

For once the clever Ph.D. could not keep quiet. He allowed himself to be drawn in. "Society will never, never change? It will always be work-centred? Always?"

"Full employment," reiterated the man from the left. "Always!"

"But I do think we shall be missing a glorious opportunity," the conservative member murmured, shaking her head slowly. She seemed to have been transformed. The co-opted teacher nodded, too, but felt surprised at this turn of events. The conservative, in turn, smiled at the puzzled socialist and then went on:

"Isn't encouraging, helping, persuading parents to bring up and teach their own children, with all the exciting aids that are added to our store each day, just what this committee ought to be doing? Taking an exhilarating step forward?"

She refused to be silenced by the socialist's stare. To him she sounded remarkably like the liberal lady excluded from the sub-committee. Her harshness had gone. It was as if she had suddenly seen the possibilities of the decades ahead: seen an almost unbelievable freedom from full-time work, a chance for parents to stay with their children and for a restoration of the family unit.

But, exhilarating or not, the step forward was one too many for the full select committee when it re-formed under Sir Sing-Along Strain. Late in 1999 it remained wedded to a policy of full employ-ment. Events were to prove the policy unrealistic - as Susan Smith was to find out only thirty years later when more time with their children was what most parents experienced and from which they and their children gained immensely.

Frau Hildegard Schmidt and the Resource Centre

A second Channel Tunnel, of immense capacity, had been opened in 2015, and a third, even larger, some ten years later. Travel between Great Britain and the rest of Europe had never been easier or cheaper. It made possible frequent cross-European educational visits and exchanges. They were commonplace.

Susan Smith always enjoyed travelling through the sixteen federal states to meet tutors and see their work. She was equally pleased to welcome colleagues to Britain. Some came accompanied by groups of pupils, some came alone on study leave. All were accommodated in community resource centres, or in field study centres, or in the homes of tutors and parents who participated in the National Media Library's schemes known as 'share a home' or 'swap a house'; schemes which the Library itself administered.

For her tutorial work during the month of December 2029, Susan was joined by her German namesake, Frau Hildegard Schmidt, a tutor in English from Stuttgart. Frau Schmidt was preparing a monograph, to be published in Munich in June 2030, on British facilities for housing personal study groups and their tutors. Throughout December Hildegard had been concentrating, most methodically, on community resource centres which, as yet, had no exact equivalent in Germany.

Susan had shown Frau Schmidt her consulting room at home, equipped for her pupils and their parents, and they had visited the newly-constructed homes of two pupils to view purpose-built learning facilities. At one, Hildegard had been pleased to see four children working in water-colours. The pupils were recalling scenes from a visit made to the home of a writer for young people and the village in which she lived. While they worked, a recording was being played of Bach's Concerto in D minor for two violins. Hildegard had watched and listened, transfixed: she loved painting and the concerto was one of her favourite Bach pieces.

Susan reminded her guest that sections of local libraries, universities, colleges, state hotels, museums and art galleries all set aside rooms for tutor panel use. Then she took Hildegard to the local community resource centre, situated two miles from her home on the same side of town. The resource centre warden, who was attending a conference on the enhancement of basic literary studies at the National Media Library at Melton Mowbray, had suggested that Susan act as Hildegard's guide.

Frau Schmidt noted that Susan's resource centre had once been a secondary comprehensive school built to a new design in 1974 to house 1500 pupils aged between eleven and eighteen. Some of the old classrooms, which had seated about thirty pupils for periods of fifty minutes at a time, had been retained as storage areas. Occasionally they were viewed by educational historians, keen to find evidence of the classroom-teaching system which had endured for so long. They saw where a single teacher, at times apprehensive, had faced a room full, perhaps, of poorly-motivated young people and taught them a slice of a pre-ordained syllabus. Sometimes, they knew, she would have met with little success despite efforts which left her drawn and exhausted. The historians, as did Susan, wondered that a system so often disliked by teacher and taught had lasted for such a long time.

"We persevered with those methods for longer than you," said Hildegard. "We were still instructing in large classes until 2015, although some towns had dispensed with it years before. Often the method lacked humanity and was frequently inefficient."

As they moved around the resource centre, Susan explained that twelve family tutor-panels, that is some 72 personal tutors and 1200 pupils, shared the educational and recreational facilities of one local community resource centre.

"Do you still separate 'educational' and 'recreational'?" asked Hildegard.

"Not really. They often merge, but the amount of such use varies considerably. Pupils tend to use the centre under the guidance of their personal tutor and parents. And then tutors themselves vary in their approach to their work and in the extent to which they need the centre. In areas of inadequate housing there is greater use - especially of the study rooms - but this is being rectified rapidly."

Susan made clear that the first function of the centre was to help personal tutors undertake work with their groups, particularly with their study of literature, art and music - the bulk of the curriculum. Tutors always had first call on the centre's services and these were available to them for fifteen hours a day throughout the year.

"There are no school holidays now, and the inconvenient and anachronistic bank holidays have long been dispensed with," Susan pointed out.

She explained carefully that with such extensive opening

times, and with varying degrees of use by tutors and pupils, there were many occasions when the centres were underused and at these times their facilities were available to members of the public. Because fixed school hours and fixed school terms no longer operated, there were times when small groups of pupils, or individuals, were studying at or enjoying the recreational facilities of the centre at the same time as other, older, people.

The two young women saw this in operation in the centre's libraries, in drama groups rehearsing, in sections of orchestras and with two string quintets practising in the centre's music wing. This healthy integration of age groups, which had eroded still further the isolation of many traditional schools, was firmly supported by the Professional Tutors' Guild. But the Guild rightly insisted that use by the public should never impinge on the work of pupils and their tutors. To this end, as Hildegard had already discovered, each community resource centre had a resident tutor-warden, one of whose duties was to ensure that priority be given to tutors' professional needs.

From the meticulous notes she had made in earlier research, and from information she had obtained from the current edition of the community resource centre handbook, Frau Schmidt knew that basic tutoring accommodation, except as an interim measure in poor localities, had been planned on the assumption that a high proportion of tutoring practice would take place in the homes of tutors and pupils. Thus basic teaching provision of a classroom type was not extensive and was used, where it existed, largely for adult education classes or meetings. The original classrooms of the old comprehensive school had been converted to other uses, and this change in accommodation design had stimulated curriculum reform in the no-schools system.

What Susan and her guest did not know, but could have discovered, was that back in 1999 a powerful lobby both inside and outside Sir Sing-Along Strain's most select committee, horrified at the idea of comparatively new schools being scrapped or sold off for a pittance, had put pressure on Sir Sing-Along to resist such waste. Tempers had flared, threats had been issued, and for a time the whole exciting teaching-without-schools project had, as late as mid-October 1999, been placed in jeopardy.

But one evening, sitting in the lounge of the expensive hotel where the most select committee was boarded, the young Ph.D. had seized eagerly on a remark made by the youngest of the co-opted ex-teacher members.

"This is nice," she had exclaimed, looking around at the elegant furnishings and decor. "A pity our poor old school staffroom wasn't a bit more like this." She had sipped her second white rum and coke, its twisted slice of lemon still intact and with enough ice left to make a gentle clinking sound in the glass. "A right dump that was ..."

"Go on," the flaxen-haired doctor of philosophy had urged, "follow it up, follow that line of thought, take it further ..."

"Staffrooms? Make them like this? But it would cost a fortune, and anyway, there won't be any ..."

"But there could be. Some of the bigger schools could be kept as leisure centres, resource areas and support buildings: they could have lounges like this, and swimming pools. Classrooms could be converted to study and tutorial rooms, boarding facilities fixed, restaurants opened. Why not? And theatre workshops, art studios, music rooms and gardens are practically there already." He had looked at her thoughtfully. "We could start with the lounges ..."

He was only six years younger than the co-opted ex-teacher and she was a most attractive woman.

"Meeting all our leisure needs?" she said, leaning back, gazing at him. There had been a lot of rum in her second drink. "How nice."

She thought how pleasant all this was. Much better than teaching! She closed her eyes sleepily and mused. In congenial surroundings such as these and after a couple of rums and a couple of cokes even Ph.D.s with flaxen hair could have appeal.

But the clever Ph.D., perhaps not quite as clever as he thought, had already begun, at 23.30, to make notes on possible architectural conversions ... the good-looking woman had given him ideas.

Thus was conceived, from a throwaway remark in a four star hotel, the idea of community resource centres. Opportunities had been taken and missed in late October 1999.

The tireless ex-sixth form master, after a week's inexorable canvassing of select committee members, had calmed fears sufficiently for the committee's work to proceed. He had stressed, *ad nauseam*, the avoidance of waste: not all schools would be sold off. That, he had said, would prevent too clamorous an outcry. Further, the provision of community facilities on the scale now envisaged, made available to the general public, would win votes by the million. Community resource centres were definitely 'in'.

Susan and Hildegard made an extensive and leisurely tour of the centre and the German tutor made notes electronically and videotaped extensively. They began with the library complex.

"There are four main libraries and a large reading-room-cum-lounge," Susan pointed out. "The first, the most extensive, is the library of literature and drama. The fiction section is truly immense and, even at 08.00, widely in use by children, tutors and members of the public. Automatic delivery of 'known and stored' titles is quietly and quickly accomplished. 'Unheld' titles are available on screen within a few minutes.

"The second, the music library, houses scores, discs and tapes as well as reference works, biographies, autobiographies and criticism. Many small, soundproofed cubicles are already occupied and there is a widespread use of headphones in the open areas.

"The library of art, which has benefited from a legacy, is one-third library and two-thirds gallery. You can see that older pupils are helping with the reorganisation of the current exhibition.

"The fourth library houses general works and national and local information data bases, and is widely used as a general reference library. In all four libraries," Susan explained, "twelve to thirteen year olds are helping the public to use computerised catalogues in the tracing of elusive sources. More than one of these pupils are considering a career in modern librarianship, although commitment is not actively encouraged by tutors for pupils of this age."

From the libraries the two women moved to the old school's large and small halls. After conversion these now provided one large and two small stages, dressing rooms, screen and projection rooms and seating for 500. With seating cleared, the halls provided floors for dances, exhibitions, sales and other social and commercial community functions. In one area Hildegard observed considerable hustle as a series of short plays, written and set to music by pupils and parents, were prepared for public performance later that week. Pupils from three tutor panels, with many adult members of relevant societies, were involved in much of this work.

The whole of one personal tutor group was helping, as part of its community work, with the planting of sapling mountain ash in the centre's appealingly landscaped grounds. Hildegard noted this as, with Susan, she made her way around the well-kept lawns to the swimming-pool, gymnasium, sports pavilion, health centre and recreation complex. Susan explained that the children, aged about twelve, were learning from their work as the centre's gardener was teaching, quietly, while together they planted that day's quota.

In addition to a standard swimming pool, they saw that there were teaching pools, instructors' and attendants' rooms, sauna, booking offices, shops and cafeteria. The gymnasium was well equipped as was the recreation or workout area. The health centre nearby served the local community and provided advice and guidance to tutors in their work with children. Activities in these centres were well under way.

The women returned by a different route, skirting playing fields and running track, to the main buildings. Hildegard commented on the comfortable lounges suggested to the clever Ph.D. thirty years earlier, and a well-furnished, finely-equipped restaurant. This provided light refreshments or full meals, all at a small profit, to tutors, pupils and public, for fourteen of the fifteen hours each day the resource centre was open.

"In the old days," Susan said, "most schools were closed for two or three months each year and in evenings and at weekends in many cases. It was quite absurd that such expensive buildings, land and facilities were so underused. And their very closure, apart from being so uneconomic, invited the attention of thieves and vandals."

"I know. We had that, too. I don't think it was as bad in Germany, but I can't be sure." Hildegard tended to be protective of her state.

They then saw other public recreation areas with facilities for cards, board games, pool and darts, and another for quiet reading and writing. Snacks were available, and the whole area, adjacent to the lounges and restaurant, was handy for visitors and groups. Nearby was a common room for tutors attached to the resource centre, and for the centre warden, support staff and guests. It had more social significance in the new system than the restricted-use staffroom of the school-based era, Hildegard was told. She spent some of her time reading noticeboards, overhearing conversations, checking rosters and making herself familiar with all that was going on.

She visited the warden's study which, together with a separate office suite, was the administrative base for the centre and the twelve tutor panels affiliated to it.

Susan had already told Hildegard that no worker in the education service was more highly paid than the fully-experienced personal tutor and that there were no exceptions to this rule. But the sight of the grand office available to the warden made Hildegard think otherwise: she still associated room size and opulent fittings with high salary and elevated status.

"No. She is paid at the same rate as the personal tutor. For her time here the warden gets a few privileges and a nice study and on-the-spot accommodation, but she more than earns it, and when her stint here is done she returns to her tutor group panel. There is no sense of promotion. No great importance is attached to educational administration," Susan insisted. "And it is not paid more. A few expenses, perhaps, but that is all, and a good thing too."

Susan had heard stories of administrators or managers in the old school system being paid three, four or five times as much as a young teacher working daily with thirty children in a classroom.

'No wonder the end came when it did,' she reflected. But she did not relate these thoughts to Hildegard. Despite their states' common membership of the European Federal Union there was still, in 2029, rivalry between citizens and a jealous guarding of the past. Indeed, in some cities the state flag still flew, proudly, side by side with the star-spangled banner of the European Union.

In the same block were offices housing clerical assistants whose work was to support the warden and personal tutors. The team, which now did so much of the mundane work teachers had once done, also provided secretarial services for the public, charged at cost. Close by, and between the offices and main library - Susan and Hildegard had almost returned to their starting point - were rows of study rooms. These were for individual pupils, or small groups, with parents, to use for private study and were allocated by tutors as they thought fit. The rooms were soundproofed and contained terminals for National Media Library lessons.

While they relaxed having coffee and gâteaux in the tutors' common room, Susan reminded her guest that all community resource centres had four dormitories, two for boys and two for girls, each accommodating twelve pupils. That was sufficient for visiting tutor groups from abroad, or from within the Federal Union, who wished to undertake field work or other projects in the centre's locality. There were four small bed-sitting rooms nearby for visiting tutors. Susan admitted to Hildegard that towards the end of the most select committee's deliberations it had been proposed to extend substantially this accommodation and upgrade it to three-star hotel standards to attract more outsiders and to provide revenue, but capital costs had prevented this and the idea was still at the 'possible future project' stage. She said the warden's flat and the assistant wardens' flats were in the same complex - a building which originally had been a school classroom teaching block.

In the grounds the women had seen houses and bungalows for

ancillary staff, particularly gardeners, caretakers, some domestic employees, and drivers of the centre's super-safe mini buses. Hildegard had been favourably impressed by this but had not said so.

'Stuttgart's sports facilities are better than these,' she thought. 'And I am in no doubt at all that the coffee we would offer a guest would be much better than this.' But she did not mention that, either.

Susan described the staffing of the resource centres, speaking clearly into Hildegard's miniature microphone as she did so.

"Each centre has about twenty employees," Susan explained. "Some work part-time. Use is also made of voluntary help from parents and others and regular help is provided by older pupils as part of their community service work. The warden," she explained, "is a fully-qualified personal tutor with considerable tutoring experience, who has full-time administrative responsibility for the centre. She is available in an advisory capacity to help parents - especially with the choice of a tutor panel. The warden helps by working in a tutor panel when time allows and when such help is agreed with tutors: she values the opportunity of renewing her tutoring skills ready for when she returns to full-time tutoring. Her duties also include visiting resource centres in other countries and states and helping with the organisation of conferences and the entertainment of foreign delegations." Susan paused. "She is helped in all this by her deputy warden who works on a part-time basis and is herself a tutor-panel chairperson. The term of office for both is four years. Wardens are elected by the twelve affiliated chairpersons. In exceptional circumstances a second consecutive appointment is allowed."

Susan drew breath here, and at the same time smiled at the sight of the German tutor recording so assiduously.

Then she described how a full-time bursar was responsible to the warden for the finances of the centre and its tutor panels. The bursar had one full-time and two part-time secretaries and they assisted chairpersons and tutors. Susan continued:

"The librarian has three qualified assistants and they administer the four centre libraries and give ongoing help to tutors. They are in daily contact with the NML and check on the daily updating of materials. These four workers are crucial," she emphasised. "They enable personal tutors to choose from a huge range of material for their individual study programmes. I couldn't manage my work without them."

Hildegard nodded. "It is the same now in Germany."

"Yet," Susan confessed, "when this scheme for teaching-without-schools was being planned back in 1999, there were terrible rows about the level of staffing being proposed for these centres. And, I was told at university, it was not until it was pointed out to some of the planners that librarians and swimming instructors, groundspersons and others were already working and being paid and that most of them would be brought into the new scheme and cost little more, that some of the money-misers relented and gave it all the O.K."

Hildegard smiled in a slightly superior fashion, but did not pursue the subject. "That was a British affair," she thought, "not ours."

But she did ask about the sports complex staff and learned that there were coaches for swimming and physical recreation who shared responsibility for teaching in, and for the supervision and administration of, the pools and gymnasium. At least one coach was on duty whenever the centre was open. They had help from qualified parents and others and from older children in associated panel groups. They helped organise team games as required.

"There is also a full-time clerical assistant whose salary comes largely from fees charged to the general public for admission."

Although she did not comment, Hildegard thought this staffing inadequate and suspected it would not be tolerated in Germany. But the community resource centres as a whole, she had been told several times, still suffered from the 1999 obsession with minimum staffing levels, and this was being reviewed under federal law.

"In the health centre nearby a full-time nurse helps with first aid and with health promotion in the centre. She liaises with local doctors and hospitals," Susan added.

She went on to say that under the supervision of the librarians, two full-time technicians edited and stored audio-visual material for use by tutors, and installed and maintained equipment.

"There are two caretaker-drivers who, in return for their combined duties, receive free accommodation at the centre in addition to their salary. They, with a well-qualified groundsperson and ten part-time cleaners, help to maintain the centre, its grounds and its mini buses. They are helped by, and can give instruction to, older pupils.

"Similarly, qualified staff in the restaurants help with teaching in their fields and are helped, in their turn, by older pupils, part-time employees, and volunteer community workers."

Susan stressed that the first duty of all staff was to help personal tutors with their work. Their second duty was to ensure that the centre was attractive to the general public, and that revenue was earned. Susan admitted that there was still some concern that educational establishments should make money, and even more that pupils should help with their maintenance. There were even now, in 2029, a few expressions of unease that skilled persons who were not fully-qualified tutors should help with teaching.

"But I think that it all reinforces important aspects of the pupils' emerging philosophy," Susan argued. "They are encouraged to see the need for each member of a community to make a contribution to the wellbeing of others. Where better to begin than at the local community resource centre?"

Susan explained, too, that all the necessary administrative arrangements for this work, including the drawing up of rosters, were made by support staff and not by personal tutors, although those tutors, and the pupils' parents, always had the legal responsibility of knowing where each child was at any one time and what he was doing. "That really is rigorously laid down."

Had she known it, Susan would have attributed the instigation of those safeguards to the disliked lawyer of 1999 and his insistence that supervision of a tutor's charges be strict and comprehensive. Unpopular though he might have been, his cautious, caring sense in this instance had won him allies and his rigid requirements had been written into statute. They had stayed there ever since.

Hildegard Schmidt did not know of this long-ago soul-searching. She could see that in every state care had to be taken at all times but especially when, as part of their community service programme, older children worked away from their usual, familiar bases. But group work in this area - of which she had seen many worthwhile examples during her stay in Britain - seemed to her to be excellent preparation for a responsible and caring adulthood.

She talked to Susan for a while about her next moves, and sipped more coffee. Hildegard was to visit several field study centres - some in cities, some in areas of outstanding natural beauty, and some in a selection of towns and villages across the country, which would give her a fair cross-section of landscape, industry, historical association and cultural variation. She had learned that these field study centres were mostly located in suitably-sized and well-placed schools retained from the old school-based system. Those schools had been converted to provide simple, basic accommodation and study facilities and each now had a full-time warden knowledgeable of the locality and who was assisted, when necessary, by part-time volunteer guides. Personal tutors were free to reserve rooms in these centres so that pupils could study interesting features of a locality at first hand and away from home. Often they were accompanied by parents and other relatives keen to help and, perhaps, to further their own knowledge at the same time.

Susan told Hildegard to note, too, that in all universities and large public libraries and museums, rooms were set aside for tutors and their pupils. In each case, a named liaison officer, librarian or curator was responsible for aiding tutors. The same was true of many youth hostels and National Trust and other properties: there was always someone eager to help.

So, duly armed with her scribbled notes, electronically recorded comments and videotapes, Hildegard offered her thanks and bade Susan farewell. Well-satisfied with her visit, she set off for her next field of study.

The German girl had to admit, as she drove away, that the British were forging ahead with their educational provision. And they were leading the way in other fields, too. A third channel tunnel, which she was to drive through on her way home, had been a great success, and from 1st January it was to be toll-free! She was glad she had remembered to buy a one-way ticket on her outward journey ... She had saved herself 39 ecus!

The National Media Library

Susan and her three colleagues were unhappy with two aspects of the teaching series they viewed prior to its general release from the National Media Library. One was the 'lecturing' tone of the media tutor: that could soon be put right. The other, more difficult to rectify, was a lack of balance between the work of the famous scientist featured and the story of her life. Both, appropriately gauged, would appeal to children, but Susan's colleagues thought unimportant aspects of the woman's work had been over-emphasised and the courage shown in her personal life played down. Susan, who was familiar with the woman's work and had read several biographies, agreed.

The difficulty of striking a balance in presentations - in any format - and of pleasing everyone - even if that was desirable - was well known to most members of Sir Sing-Along's committee at the time the National Media Library's constitution was debated. It was one of the more intransigent problems among the many they tried, with some acrimony, to resolve.

Susan knew that the resource centre warden could be told of their concern and that representations could be made to the Programme Review Board responsible for evaluation of all NML productions. They would be exercising rights of criticism written into the Education Act of 2000 at the behest of the select committee.

When it was proposed, in 1999, that teaching material for the new no-schools scheme be centrally produced, stored and transmitted, there had been alarm expressed at the influence and power this could invest in producers, editors and other NML staff.

"We've got more than enough bias in the media now," protested the portly conservative. "If you think we're going to let our children," and she glowered at the chairman, "be influenced by a few unaccountable, faceless . . ."

"Too left-wing for you, is it, the media?" stormed the sceptical socialist. "Why don't you mention the influence of big business and the advertising whizz kids? Don't start shouting at the workers. Influence? Don't you talk to us about influence!"

Sir Sing-Along reeled at their railing. Weren't Britain's media the best in the world? How he had howled at *Yes Minister.* He had bought every episode for his sister last Christmas. Where else could you get such programmes? What was wrong with these people?

The good knight sought help and the young Ph.D. suggested

that members should list all the safeguards they would need before agreeing to a National Media Library being established. Then they could write the most basic ones into the new National Education Bill called for by the Cabinet. In the meantime he would present his paper outlining the structure of the NML. Against this atmosphere of profound suspicion, he proposed they examine the less contentious issues. They settled, eventually, to a reading of his paper. He was eloquent about a delightful 1820's country house set in 150 acres of mature parkland on the borders of Leicestershire and the reinstated county of Rutland. This peaceful park was located in an area soon to be made easily and quietly accessible via extensions to the electro-rail and truck-free parkway network planned for 2008. The old house would be sympathetically adapted to its new use and have studios, editing rooms, libraries, production laboratories and transmission stations. It would offer superb accommodation to its regular staff, resource centre wardens, visiting tutors and tutors on temporary short-stay secondment. There would be viewing theatres, seminar and meeting rooms, restaurants, a massive tree-screened car park, herds of gently grazing deer, a lake with rare and colourful fowl . . ."

"And the money?" came from two members questioning in unison.

"The sale of twenty large city-centre comprehensives will easily cover everything needed and more . . ."

"Why visiting tutors? Sounds like a skive . . ."

"A 'skive'?"

"Means a perk . . . bit of a doddle," explained the tired trade unionist, drowsily. Where had this lot been educated?

"Visiting tutors' presence and involvement," said the Ph.D., "will be one of the safeguards we are to discuss later. They will check what is produced, why, for whom, when and how its use is proposed and what guidance notes are compiled. But why don't we get on to the benefits of the NML? There are so many."

The co-opted ex-teacher from further education described what these would be. He had clearly been liaising with the London Ph.D.

He claimed one distinct advantage would be the high quality of lessons prepared for tutors' consideration. The viewing of a current, 1999, TV natural history film indicated illustration, demonstration and elucidation far beyond the capacities of a classroom teacher preparing work on her own. That huge gap had been widening as media techniques improved while teachers' time was spent more and more on proliferating administration. A painstakingly produced professional reading of an extract from a novel or production of a scene from a play, would greatly enhance the enjoyment and understanding of both book and drama. By means of the NML, all would be available as soon as the personal tutor felt its use was beneficial or when her pupils thought a repeat viewing would help them. Explanation of points in maths and science, made on screen and supported by notes in print, would often be clearer to pupils than either the teacher's or textbook writer's attempts had been to do the same thing in the past. In practice, each would tend to be of help to the other. He stressed, however, that no matter how good the media's teaching technology became, it would never replace the personal tutor. Only the tutor, working with parents, would know fully the pupil's individual needs and be able to satisfy them at that pupil's level: only the personal tutor would be able to talk to the child in terms he understood about matters which were important to him. Members accepted this, although one or two noted points for later clarification.

The ex-teacher from further education went on to say that these advantages would increase as tutors became skilled in the use of the programmes and began to appreciate their range and potential. Some tutors, he suggested, would themselves become producers of programmes and would use their talents and their professionalism to ensure that lessons were pupil-tutor oriented. With knowledgeable and critical personal tutors submitting regular reports to NML, programmes would be under scrutiny and amended as determined by the strength of demand. Tutors' programme notes would be changed too.

Thus tutors would know that the NML's work would be under their surveillance. Although using material prepared by others they would be instrumental in its revision and in the creation of new programmes. Professionally they would influence what was produced and how it was used.

The most select committee accepted this without undue antipathy. They were reassured.

One of the other co-opted ex-teachers said that as tutors pre-viewed and used NML lessons and became familiar with them they would think of new ways of using them with pupils. They would know, also, that the lesson was instantly available and this would lead to greater tutor confidence. They would become less dependent on their own, limited, lesson preparation, and be using, with adaptation, others' proven, tested material. She said the school-based system, in which the teacher was sometimes unable to justify wholeheartedly the relevance of what was being offered, would be avoided. In such situations, teachers in the old system were likely to have been on the defensive in front of classes and so work-related stress had grown.

Also avoided would be the need for pupils to study set topics at set times. She said the long-term forward planning of school time-tables could not have taken into account the personal predilections of teachers and pupils weeks or months ahead. There are times when individuals do not wish to read a novel, view a film, listen to music, study history, ponder maths problems or throw javelins on a sportsfield. These fluctuating personal disinclinations can arise from a variety of causes, many inexplicable and none, necessarily, reprehensible. She asked why thirty fifteen year olds should all read Act I of *The Merchant of Venice* at 10.45 on Tuesdays? Or all run around a gym an hour later because that is what an arbitrary timetable called for? The system itself must answer that. But such practices could do more harm than good.

One committee member demanded the speaker be kept to the subject, but the ex-teacher pressed on and said that the arrival of small personal tutor groups in a non-school environment and the use of individual study-programmes made possible by NML and world-wide multi-media developments would eradicate the rigid school timetabling absurdities that were often such an obstacle to enjoyable learning. Education could become more humane . . .

"You are being swept along on waves of your own enthusiasm, madam . . ."

"No, sir. Can you deny that the NML and media networks will be able to provide huge scope for the capable and imaginative tutor in her work? But," she paused deliberately, "conversely, failure to provide worthwhile study programmes will be the tutor's own fault. Traditional excuses - like blaming the headteacher, or the timetable, or the educational publishers, or the local authority, or the exam-inations board - will no longer hold good."

She went on to say that different pupils would take different lessons in the same study period. The tutor would thus be able to decide what was studied, when and where. The second advantage would be just as great as the first. The tutor could work alongside one pupil or several and discuss, encourage, elaborate, question and assess. The tutor would be fully professional . . .

"That point is being made *ad nauseam* and is overstated . . ."

"It cannot be overstated. We must do all we can to ensure that tutors move towards full professional status and a big step will be insisting that the tutor be directly responsible to parents for the work that is done having regard to her knowledge of the child and his circumstances, and the mass of material available."

But several members of the select committee were unconvinced. They tapped the table quietly with their fingernails. The argument was carried forward by the young Ph.D. He was worried. At that moment he was not sure of a majority.

Anxiously he argued that there must be trust between the caring, skilled tutor and the pupil and parents. But the trust had to go further. The state, too, had to have trust in the tutor and give her the professional opportunity to do what she thought best for the child without restrictions - apart from those basic tenets implanted in law. Without that trust the full benefits of the new scheme - or any scheme - would not be realised. He, too, waited. There were no interjections. So he continued persuasively, keen to reassure.

With slowly increasing confidence he reminded the committee that all lessons would be available for public reception, that comments would be invited and the NML would be required to consider them. Parents would be provided with advance copies of their child's study-programme, and could view with their child or on their own. Parents could become so well-informed about the content that they could help their children every day, and as a matter of course. Supplementary material, some stocked at the community resource centre, would also be available to parents. They would be able to discuss programmes informally with other parents and tutors. This often incidental discussion, because of its informality, would be invigorating, uninhibited and full of value to parents, tutors and the NML.

Pupils and parents would quickly learn how to key-in recommended lessons according to simple codes given with their personal study programmes. They would be able to repeat lessons - or parts of lessons - according to their needs, or be able to take additional explanatory or supplementary practice lessons. They would be able to assess their progress in an enjoyable, non-threatening way. They would follow up points in tutorials with their personal tutor or with another tutor suggested by her as one having special understanding of that work and the problems it could give rise to.

The young Ph.D. admitted, quietly and frankly, that the NML would be expensive to establish, but the cost would be fully justified because programmes prepared and stored would be available, if selected, to hundreds of tutors and thousands of pupils and parents. Much of the material would last for years. Frequent revision would be a relatively easy and cost-effective matter.

The most select committee, tired at the end of a long day, noted the points about expense, but the speaker's voice was soft and compelling, and the day itself had been unseasonably warm. The air conditioning was only partially effective and its background noise - a persistent, low humming sound - was sleep inducive. Members nodded through the points about capital expenditure and then sought refreshment on the broad terraces overlooking the river. The relieved Ph.D. smiled and helped Sir Sing-Along with his portfolio.

Early next morning the most select committee considered the safeguards that were to be built into the system and from which Susan and her pupils were to profit significantly decades later.

Aware of their time limit, and to keep matters moving, the young Ph.D. agreed with the foodstore magnate that the new system would offer no panacea. There would be faults in the plan and in the people operating it. So, as in her business empire, the magnate demanded ongoing scrutiny and screening. She got them. They were incorporated in the final Bill.

The pallid parent-governor representative, who became daily more enamoured of the National Media Library, admitted that there would be dangers in too heavy a dependence on centrally-transmitted lessons vested in the hands of a small editorial and scheduling staff, but said she believed that, with the committee's commendable forethought, these could be avoided.

There was a pause. Then the foodstore magnate spoke again. Despite her doubts about the scheme as a whole, she was in favour of centralised stockholding and efficient distribution. She seemed to see the NML in this way: a streamlined, direct and cost-effective machine for the prompt delivery of teaching material.

"It's nothing of the sort . . ." exploded the irate ex-headteacher. "It's . . ." But she stopped. 'Why alienate an unexpected ally?' she thought. "Yes," she said slowly as if reconsidering her position. "Yes, yes . . . I see what you mean."

Then the conservative MP made a well thought-out contribution to the debate. Her daughter had been a teacher for a year before giving up the work when a nervous breakdown threatened. The MP had had much sympathy with teachers' conditions then despite what she saw as continual moaning about pay and pensions.

"Let's take this serenely," she offered. "Let's all agree that this teaching-without-schools proposal has great possibilities. But let's admit, too, that there will be problems."

She looked around. The disliked lawyer was suspicious. Was this lady changing sides? The sceptical socialist was also suspicious: in his view conservatives never changed sides; they only appeared to do so occasionally for self-serving purposes.

"Sometimes, in the past," she said, "the latest idea in education has been hailed as the final answer - the ultimate solution to schools' and schoolteachers' every problem. Yet obvious difficulties in implementation and practice were ignored. The mildest objectors were labelled 'reactionary' when all they were trying to do was point out transparent drawbacks."

Several select committee members approved.

"This all fed teacher cynicism. So much was lost which could have been gained if the claims for the new approaches had been realistic, difficulties realised, and issues faced with honesty. The wholesale introduction of mixed-ability grouping was a case in point."

The sceptical socialist sniffed.

"All I ask is that we recognise the dangers as well as the benefits of using heavily the new technology. It will be no cure-all."

Half the members applauded gently. The others sat stony-faced. But all went on to examine the list of safeguards prepared by the secretaries and their advisors. They had noted that wardens of the community resource centres, in unison with tutor panel chairpersons, would arrange seminars for tutors at which NML material would be evaluated. Reports would be sent to the Library. The value of the follow-up work suggested, along with the reactions of pupils to lessons already taken, would be assessed. Seminars would be held for parents and views would be exchanged. Such professional and public involvement would counter hints of indoctrination or tendencies to transmit unsuitable material.

Then, during their professional training, personal tutors would be made aware of the need for caution. They would learn to use, constructively and critically, lessons emanating from a single source. Emphasis would be laid on the need for tutors to make use of their own, their pupils' and their fellow tutors' widely varying interpretations of lessons. They would learn ways of encouraging pupils to criticise material even if, at times, the criticism had to be tutor-initiated and sustained. Older pupils would be taught to evaluate lessons as part of their media studies programme - itself a vital part of the language arts. They would apply the critical skills learned formally to the critical assessment not only of their lessons but to the wider media output met in their everyday experiences.

"The quality of their lives may well depend on their abilities in that direction," said the liberal lady, and no-one disagreed.

Pupils, parents and tutors would also debate ways in which individual or group follow-up activities could be devised from NML lessons taken, and these variations in approach would, in themselves, act as an antidote to uniformity in the use of broadcast material. And the very compass of the material available would help avoid regimentation in compiling personal study programmes.

As an essential requirement for professional qualification, tutors would have to show that they were conversant with the whole range of what was available from the NML and how it could be traced and cross-referenced. Eventually, personal tutors would become adept at constructing well-balanced study programmes. They would learn that this new knowledge of what was available and the skills acquired in making good its use, would largely replace the subject-based knowledge and teaching methods demanded of their school-based predecessors.

The members listened carefully, and then another of the co-opted ex-teachers referred to a second list of safeguards. During their professional education, she expounded, student-tutors would be helped to see the many possibilities of NML material. They would learn that lessons would rarely be used in the same way by any two pupils or tutors and that interesting interpretations would emerge that had not been envisaged by programme editors or producers. This would be a further safeguard against widespread control of pupils' lesson material emanating from central sources.

All personal tutors and trainee tutors would be expected to contribute ideas for lesson series. They would advise on preparation at various stages. The tutor would be involved in the work of the NML to provide for her own professional satisfaction and to ensure that select groups of NML tutor-producers did not acquire unacceptable degrees of influence. Yet further safeguards would be the replacement of NML staff after stipulated periods in office, and the presence of temporarily-attached chairpersons who wished to undertake NML work during sabbaticals. No tutor would regard herself as a passive receiver of other tutors' lesson material.

All this was approved with some relief by select committee

members. Some were jubilant that a major area of criticism seemed to have been taken care of. They went on to consider NML staff.

Senior permanent editing and production staff would all be qualified experienced personal tutors. None would be engaged until she had worked in a tutor panel for at least four years. Then, once appointed to the Library, the member would be required to leave the Library staff, on secondment, for a two year period in every ten years of her career and in that period would resume work as a tutor-panel member. There would be no exceptions to this rule even for the most gifted producer. Nor would there be any deviation from the rule that no person would be paid more than the experienced personal tutor working with a full quota of pupils, although the NML worker would receive expenses as well as tutor fees. In this way the status of media workers would not be inflated and there would be no pecuniary advantage in leaving tutoring for work in any other sphere of education.

Further, the select committee heard, the NML would be governed by an independent council of thirty-five people which would, as a last resort, appoint and dismiss staff, monitor the use of funds and adjudicate on programmes where there was evidence of serious disagreement or complaint. The council would be drawn from the Professional Tutors' Guild, resource centre wardens, panel chairpersons, parent committees, central and local government and the NML permanent staff. The composition would be such that a majority was always drawn from the tutoring profession, and this would ensure that the NML met the needs of children in the four to thirteen age range and that material was free of political, religious or commercial bias. The council's role would be to support tutors in their work while keeping a watchful eye on what was produced.

It was to the review council, in 2029, that the resource centre warden could have taken Susan's comments about the previews she and her colleagues had monitored. But it was not necessary. The matter was settled long before the council had to intervene. Many similar criticisms of the programmes had been filed together with suggestions for the material's improvement, and an assistant to the producer had already set in motion moves towards revision. The lessons were later used, suitably interpreted, by many Susan Smiths for the benefit of thousands of young pupils. The fears of some on the select committee had proved groundless; the machinery they had installed to safeguard pupils proved to be exactly what was needed.

8. Colleges of Middle and Later Education

Before Susan Smith viewed the National Media Library's pre-release programmes with the three colleagues from her tutor panel - a meeting she had arranged for 19.30 - she visited the father of one of her pupils, Mr Dewi Frett. Ostensibly the meeting, at his home and at his instigation, was to discuss his son's half-yearly progress report before it was finalised and filed, but, as so often happened with parental meetings, other issues were raised and more time was taken than the hour Susan usually allowed.

Susan arrived at 18.15. Mr Frett, now a single parent, had left a message on Susan's videophone to say he might be delayed for a few minutes at his office. He did not want Susan to worry, wait around unnecessarily or drive away. He did not want her to think him discourteous or unreliable, or to imagine that he did not take tutorial meetings sufficiently seriously. Yet before he phoned he hesitated in case he might disturb the tutor in her other work!

Timothy was sent to his room while parent and tutor talked about his studies and then, at greater length, about what seemed to be signs in the boy's behaviour of an increasing nervousness. Recently symptoms had 'noticeably worsened', Mr Frett said.

Susan knew, from her two years' tutoring of Timothy and from what she had learned from other panel members, that the boy's father was an exceptionally apprehensive man and had become more so since the separation from his wife two years earlier. He had appeared tense on the videophone recording. To some extent, she guessed, this disability was being passed on to Timothy, the youngest and most vulnerable of the three Frett children. Timothy's sisters and his many cousins were all far more resilient to disruption than Timothy. The several families were well known to the panel's tutors, and the chairperson had twice sought advice from the psychologist available to the panel. Most of the children had passed through the practice, and its tutors, together with staff from the resource centre had, if only in their role as concerned, trained and experienced listeners, been of great help to several members of the families but particularly to Dewi Frett.

Now Mr Frett was worrying about the prospects for Timothy's education when the boy left Susan's personal group in a few weeks' time, and he was already becoming anxious about what his son would do when he left the tutor panel to begin at middle education college four years after that. Susan realised that her job that evening was to reassure the father rather than assess the son.

'But that's how things are,' she thought. 'The two things go together and that's why my work is so important ...' And, she might have added, so varied, interesting and rewarding.

She reminded Mr Frett that Timothy woud not be leaving the tutor panel for another four years and that even then contact would not be lost. The built-in continuity between early education (4-13 years) and middle education (14-15) and later education (16-17) had been ensured when the 1999 select committee had accepted the liberal lady's proposal that personal tutors be encouraged to undertake part-time work teaching in the middle education colleges for fourteen and fifteen-year olds. She had said that this would benefit pupils through continuing contact with early education tutors.

"Not all children are of the same maturity level at a given age," she had argued, "and some are very young for their years at fourteen: it would help if they were to see their previous tutors around the big, strange buildings that are to be their first colleges."

She had stressed, too, that such commitments, voluntarily made, would enrich the personal tutors' roles and give an element of steady progression to their professional work. There had been no gainsaying that, although the employers' suave representative had thought that they were in danger of turning out a generation of namby-pambies coddled against everything. The tired trades-union spokesman had thought the same but he was too weary to speak. The liberal lady's proposal had been nodded through.

The most select committee had decided that middle and later education colleges would publish lists of courses offered and of tutors working on them. Where courses did not attract a full complement of young students, places would be offered - on payment of a cost-only fee - to adults. Their presence would emphasise further the 'college' nature of the new institution and its difference from the schools of the past.

In middle education colleges (two years) and in later education colleges (two years), the courses offered would be taught along more traditional lines than in early education. They would be divided into three categories: (i) courses where emphasis would be on the development of academic and intellectual skills; (ii) courses where studies would be of a general nature and, or, have emphasis on the furthering of leisure interests; and (iii) courses which would aim at helping the college and the community in practical ways.

For three years after that, students would attend university or join a recognised work training scheme. Thus education would continue for every citizen until at least the age of twenty-one.

"Perhaps some form of national service after that?" had suggested the portly conservative. "Perhaps two years for everyone?"

"Perhaps not," had yelled the sceptical and now irate socialist.

"Not for a year?"

"Not for a week."

"I learned a lot from my national service," claimed the employers' suave representative.

"I'm sure you did," agreed the liberal lady with a sad smile. "But national service now isn't really on. The climate isn't right."

"It's not," said the worried Ph.D. "And it's not within our remit."

"It certainly isn't," the chairman had reiterated hurriedly. "Nor, I think, is this whole middle and - what is it? - this later education business? How did we get onto this?"

"The select committee is simply suggesting an avenue. The public might want to know what happens after the age of thirteen."

The liberal lady had helped the chairman placate the meeting and it had moved gingerly to its next item, all those years ago.

Now, as she and Dewi Frett talked, Susan sensed that Timothy's future in further education was not the topmost worry on Mr Frett's long list. He was concerned about Timothy's possible move from Susan's personal group to the 10-11 year age group tutored by Harry Harty, B.C.S.(Hons), a cheerful, outgoing and well-meaning man who tended to believe everyone was as extrovert as he. During his professional training this tendency had been regarded by some professors as a weakness in a personal tutor's make-up and attempts had been made to appraise Mr Harty of their concern. But Mr Frett was unaware of these niceties in a tutor's training.

"I'm not sure how well Timothy will make out with Mr Harty," he said. "The boy seems so shy and withdrawn. It was all right with Deirdre and Daphne, my daughters." Susan nodded: she knew them well. "They got on all right with him, but they're different - more like their mother. And that was before Dulcie and I split up: when the home was still one. Things have got worse with Timothy since then."

He paused. "What I'm really getting round to asking," he said, pouring more tea, nervously, "is whether you would let Timothy stay, if it's allowed, that is, in your personal group? Stay for another two years? Or one year? Or even six months? Could it be done?"

"It could be done, and there are precedents," said Susan. "The only factor taken into account, as you know, is what is best for the child. We would all have to think about it. But yes, you have every right to choose a tutor for your boy, you know that, but it is usually - nearly always - for a two year period."

Timothy's father and Susan talked for over an hour and agreed to meet again when Susan had discussed the request with colleagues. She knew Mr Frett was one of the world's worst worriers, but she believed he might have a real problem here, and not just one that he had dwelt on and exaggerated in the absence of his wife.

The couple had separated just before Timothy came to Susan's personal group and Susan could see that in the boy's eyes she might have replaced his mother. She had shown a special interest in him, it was true, but not much more than she showed any newcomer to her group. However the boy was not to know that, and even the fact that she was at least ten years younger than Mrs Frett would have meant little to a boy of eight. She would have to be careful. She could sympathise with the arguments in favour of and against the father's appeal but, as her own reading, professional training and plain common sense all warned her, she had to avoid rushing decisions. The question would need careful consideration by her panel and some resource centre staff and, possibly, by the psychologist and social workers available to the centre. Even the social psychiatrist could be called on to advise.

But the matter would be thrashed out. People were aware. They were aware not only of important personal issues such as this, but of less critical ones too. Susan felt, from what she had heard, that these matters could now be dealt with in ways not always open to schoolteachers in the old system. She knew quite intimately her own small personal group of nineteen pupils and their families. She knew of many of their strengths and weaknesses and of the children's deep need, above all, for love, affection, concern and care.

In this instance Timothy's father had, himself, highlighted the difficulty, but Susan had been conscious of it already. If the father had not spoken first it could have been brought to the fore, perhaps less easily, by a pertinent move from her. Consideration of the boy's personal reading programme could have made broachable a difficult subject: Susan could have discussed with the father - and the mother if she was interested - the work Timothy was doing. Parts of his writing, illustration, dramatisation and further reading all could have related, in some degree, to broken families, children's uncertainties, worries, insecurity, and the agony of divided loyalties. Apposite titles could have been added, deliberately, to his reading schedule. Some of these methods might yet be used to help Timothy now that the father had given Susan the opening she needed.

The delayed start and the unexpected length of the meeting with Dewi Frett made Susan late for her previewing of material with her colleagues. But they would wait. They all knew very well what the priorities were. The media centre's programmes could be delayed, too. They could even, if necessary, be retimed and rescreened and viewed on another occasion when the recipients were ready. That was another bonus of the system. The tutors did not say so then, for they did not really know, that Sir Sing-Along's most select committee with its liberal lady, sceptical socialist, disliked lawyer, foodstore magnate and all the others, had not done so badly with the media after all.

A New Profession

The mother of a boy in Susan's personal group talked to her one afternoon about her seventeen-year-old niece, Patience Payes, who had hopes of becoming a personal tutor. The boy's mother asked Susan about the girl's prospects and the course she had to follow.

"We know she should be proficient on a musical instrument, have wide interests, and that she has to go to university to gain a Bachelor of Arts or Bachelor of Combined Studies degree," the girl's aunt said, "and then do several years' training after that. But her parents are worried because by that time she will be twenty-four and may not finally qualify even then. And if she does, she may not like the job and go off to do something else."

"There's not too much danger of that," Susan responded. "The selection procedure for tutorships is rigorous in the early stages. If she is not suitable she will soon be discouraged from continuing. As for the three years getting her degree, that's never time wasted. Apart from the value of the study itself, she can use her B.A. or B.C.S. degree for entry to many other occupations. Remember how important the arts are today."

The aunt seemed unconvinced.

"Tell her to get in touch and I'll talk to her," said Susan. "At the same time she can come here and see the work I do. She can visit the resource centre with me, as well."

"That's what I hoped you'd say," said the girl's aunt with a smile.

"Then you should have come straight out with it: we've known each other long enough and well enough for that, I hope." Although there was a smile on her face, too, Susan was unhappy that, despite the close, friendly relationships she thought she had established with all the parents of children in her group, this mother was reluctant to make openly such a reasonable request. She would need to rethink this state of affairs for a day or so. It was not good to have indications of hesitancy in an area where she was in a position to offer informed advice.

Susan knew that Patience had, from the ages of four to thirteen, been a pupil in a tutor panel in a neighbouring town and she thought it would be good for her to see how a different panel worked. Approaches, qualifications, specialities, accommodations, reading lists could all be so different. No two panels were ever alike.

Patience visited Susan one evening and, after permission had been obtained, was allowed to sit in on a discussion held in Susan's consulting room between the tutor and the parents of non-identical twins. Both twins were in Susan's personal group. When the parents had left, Susan asked Patience for her opinion.

"They seemed very reluctant to admit that one child is more advanced academically than the other," she offered. "You had quite a job getting them to accept that one boy needed to be doing more advanced work. They couldn't take that - especially the father?"

"Exactly," agreed Susan. "And that is how it has been for the past year. They both think nine is too young an age to be differentiating. But it isn't. Just look through the boys' work-folders and reports and you will see we're already at the stage where one is being held back by the other. That cannot go on, so what do we do?"

Patience examined the work discussed earlier with the parents. Unskilled as she was, the girl soon saw what Susan meant.

"But you have to remember the parents' difficulty," Susan reminded her. "They have to answer questions, perhaps quite awkward questions, when they are at home. Some leading questions from the boys can't be easy to answer without hurting one or the other or even upsetting the grandma who lives close by!"

She paused.

"So I try to extend one child - almost surreptitiously - through careful choice of books and in setting the work that arises. At the same time, as I was doing this evening, I am getting the parents gradually to accept, I hope, that differences exist and may widen. But you have to be so careful not to hurt people. It's delicate work."

"But fascinating?"

"And worthwhile. You soon find out that the children and their families are so dissimilar. They need individual treatment. No," she hesitated for a moment. "'Treatment' isn't quite the right word. 'Counselling' perhaps, or 'guidance', or 'help'. Yes, 'help' is the one: they all need individual help. The simplest word is best - as usual! You help both as a professional and as a friend."

Susan smiled in a kindly way. Patience, a quiet, sensible and sensitive girl, smiled too, but uncertainly. There was perplexity in her expression and anxiety in her questions.

"That's what I would have to do? Work as delicately as that? On my own?"

"Eventually, when you've really decided what you want to do. When you're older and properly trained. And you would not be on your own. Tutors are never working entirely on their own. There's always help close at hand: there has to be. Anyway, that's all years away. Maybe we'd better talk about those years and what you're going to do with them."

They made coffee. Patience looked through more of the work Susan's group was doing. Even though she had been a student within a tutor panel herself for ten years, Patience was surprised by the variety of the reading and associated work that was being done. The level of reading and comprehension of most of the children was notably high. Until now she had seen a tutor panel only from the perspective of a single pupil - herself; today she was able to see it from the viewpoint of nineteen children plus their tutor. She was quite excited.

"Let's walk to the resource centre," suggested Susan. "Although the centre's the one you made use of as a pupil, you can go round it with me and see it as a prospective tutor. It won't be the same!"

As they walked they talked about a tutor's training and qualifications. Susan said that those aspiring to become tutors read for an acceptable arts or combined studies degree at any university within the European Union, or abroad. If the latter, the Professional Tutors' Guild (PTG) had to agree that such a university's honours degrees were of an adequate standard.

"There has been a change recently," she said. "In addition to the B.A. or B.C.S. degrees, the social sciences have become eligible. One that has become immensely popular is the sociology of literature. A friend of mine read for one a few years ago and wrote his special topic paper on a mid-1950s satirical novel called *Lucky Jim* by Kingsley Amis. Behind the humour lay much that made him think about the social and academic life of the provincial university of that time. He and his tutor found that really intriguing, and so did I."

"I'd like to read it," said Patience.

"You can," said Susan, smiling. "It's still in print after seventy-five years - not bad for a novel set in the world of higher education!"

Susan returned to the present as they toured the resource centre. Between comments on what they saw, Susan explained that if the budding personal tutor obtained a first or second class honours degree she was invited to informal talks with panel chairpersons and a resource-centre warden near to her home or university. The student was responsible for initiating the talks, and these included frank discussions on the nature of the work and the demands of the training to be followed.

"Absolutely no soft options," stressed Susan.

She said that at this stage the talks were for the benefit of the prospective student and went unrecorded. They were exploratory and for her guidance and could last for hours.

If she then remained interested in tutoring as a long-term career, she would make formal application to a regional office of the Professional Tutors' Guild for initial registration. Susan explained that the PTG was the professional body responsible for regulating entry to the profession. "It now has the same standing as the British Medical Association has had for nearly two hundred years, and was set up in 2006 after years of bickering.

"Each regional PTG has its own tutor-education and training sub-committee one of whose duties is to assess applications and follow up references. Obligatory among referees is the university tutor best known to the candidate and the personal tutor of the candidate for her final years of pre-university education. Unless both give favourable reports the application is turned down."

Patience did not realise how powerful the PTG was as the regulatory body. Not only did it admit members, but it maintained a strict code of practice and could discipline, suspend or disqualify members. But Susan did not elaborate on this.

Instead she explained that if references were good enough the candidate attended a series of interviews lasting a week. She was accommodated in a resource centre unfamiliar to her, spending two days with each of two personal groups and then a further two days undertaking a variety of tasks in a resource centre or field station or on visits to other personal groups and tutors. During this time she was under close observation. Finally, for a whole day, she would attend formal interviews with a committee of seven dominated by panel chairpersons and a resource centre warden. At the end of the interviews and assessments each panel member would be asked a simple question: 'Do you want this person to be a personal tutor to groups of twenty children for the next thirty years?'

"And then?" asked Patience.

Susan looked at her: she could see how anxious the girl had become.

"Don't worry," she said. "This care in selection is for everyone's good - the children's, the candidates', and the profession's. There is no point in baulking at the issue: no point at all in taking on people who are going to be unhappy in their work. If the committee gives a simple majority vote of 'Yes' to the candidate, she is accepted for training. If it is four to three against, she is allowed to apply again the following year, otherwise she is out."

"I don't think I could stand all that," Patience said. "I would be so nervous. I couldn't last a whole week."

"But it is all quite gently paced and everyone is kind. And it's all for the common good. It's no earthly use letting people through who are not suitable, or not up to the job, or who are not going to do well by the children. It sounded awful to me when I was first told. But I quite enjoyed my week in the end. Really I did." And she grinned at the girl's obvious disbelief.

"And it is so important to get it right. It has to be a thorough, lengthy procedure. It wasn't always like that, you know, far from it. It has taken a great deal of effort to build up public confidence in the tutor-selection procedure."

Susan then went on to describe how, in the first stage of the course, the registered student-tutor spends one year at a university school of education taking intensive pre-professional courses in seven areas: child development and learning theories as applied to small personal groups of students; the concept of educability; the nature of literacy and numeracy; distance learning; curriculum development through individual study programmes; relationships between tutor, pupil and parents, and the transmission of social values. At the same time she continues with her musical instrument and begins to learn how it can be taught."

"And are there exams in all those?"

"In everything except the musical instrument. There are pass-fail examinations, oral, objective and open-ended, on all seven aspects. One re-sit is allowed in one topic if the other six are passed first time. A second failure leads to withdrawal from the course."

Thirty years earlier, in 1999, the ex-teachers on Sir Sing-Along's committee had been adamant that the professional training offered to tutors in the new system of education would have to be an immense improvement on the teacher-training methods of the past.

"They were constantly criticised, always under review and never really sorted out," one member had said disgustedly. "The very aims of the courses were sometimes unclear and students were dissatisfied. So were many tutors."

Partly because of this unhappy record he and others had insisted that preparation for entry to the new profession was to be lengthy, comprehensive and rigorous.

"Especially rigorous," had been the cry of the conservative lady.

"As rigorous as the training of a doctor or dentist or architect . . ."

"Or barrister," had been the disliked lawyer's widely anticipated contribution.

"Or barrister if you insist," the lady had retorted. "Remember a badly trained tutor in the new system will be capable of doing far more harm than a badly trained anybody else even though it might not be immediately and obviously apparent to the general public."

There had been no argument about this. Encouraged, she had continued:

"Weak candidates should never be accepted. If they are, by mistake, we need to know who has made the mistake, and the weak candidates should be weeded out. The needs of the children for competent and dedicated tutors will far outweigh the personal needs of a few doubtful characters for safe jobs for the rest of their lives."

She had glared challengingly at the select committee. "We may have to be cruel to be kind," she had added.

Although there had been no outright objections to the gist of her call, some members had disliked her tone and the committee had been visibly unhappy. Then, the mood having been set, there had been open disagreement about the sequence of two later stages of the training. To make matters worse, as rancour grew, members had begun to ally themselves with others of their own political persuasion: something the London Ph.D. had long feared.

He had tried to remain calm, worried as he was. Things had gone so well up to now, with the likeable and harmless Sir Sing-Along prodding them gently on their way, that the Ph.D. thought they were almost home. But he knew that things could go woefully wrong in the final stages of a campaign, especially when everyone was weary; then the wrecking issue could be quite an insignificant one compared with all that had gone before. Was his 'no-schools' plan still in danger? Could they refer the whole matter back to the House as being: 'Undecided. No agreement reached.'?"

It had been accepted already, tentatively, but with some ill will, that students who completed satisfactorily the university year should go on to stage two and spend a year working with four tutor groups: three months with each. The carefully chosen groups would be in different panels and social areas in order to widen the experience of the student. A period would be spent with four different age groups and would include one with four to five year olds and one with twelve to thirteen year olds: the youngest and oldest. The student would need to gain satisfactory reports from each of the four personal tutors with whom she worked and also from her visiting and supervising university tutor. Failure to gain five sound reports would mean withdrawal from the course. There had been relatively little trouble with that and the committee had seemed to relax again.

"So, after one - and certainly after two - unsatisfactory sessions, the student might as well withdraw straight away?" the sceptical socialist had asked. He, too, was anxious to see higher standards.

"Exactly," the disliked lawyer had replied before the food store magnate could intervene. "No point at all in going on: no vacillation."

But, later, controversy had re-emerged. An amendment had been insisted on, after some of the most acrimonious exchanges that had taken place so far, whereby a student gaining four satisfactory reports could appeal to a sub-committee of the PTG for the chance to extend her probation. The disliked lawyer, supported this time by two of the co-opted ex-teachers, had objected to this as marking the beginning of a 'watering down' policy, but they had lost the argument. They had barely concealed their anger.

Susan and Patience ended their tour and sat for a while in the tutors' lounge.

Susan paused for a moment in her narration while Patience sipped unsweetened black coffee and took in her new surroundings. Susan remembered how stories still abounded of increasingly bitter divisions in that most select of committees. The major crisis, the one the clever Ph.D. had feared, had finally come when some members had wanted the one year's probationary work with groups to precede the year of largely theoretical study at a university school of education, while others, equally vehemently, had wanted the order reversed. There was still, well into Susan's time as a tutor, controversy on this point.

But late in 1999, even the clever and increasingly apprehensive London Ph.D. had been unable to resolve the issue either by appeasing both parties himself or by suggesting to Sir Sing-Along Strain a compromise the good knight might put. You could not compromise about which year preceded which. Stalemate had been reached; the dreaded moment had come.

"Voting will be equal, sir," he had murmured to the now bewildered chairman of noble rank. "You will need to use your casting vote."

"Great Heavens," the knight had cried. "I can't take sides. Besides," and he had lowered his voice as he addressed the Ph.D., "I don't know enough about it. And what's all the fuss?"

He had raised his voice and addressed the gathering.

"Do we need to divide, ladies and gentlemen? Is it that important?"

The ferocity of the looks from around the table assured him it was. Further, that neither side intended to give way.

"An impasse, sir," the fearful Ph.D. had muttered, wretchedly. "A complete impasse."

The chairman had felt his temper rising swiftly. This ridiculous division of opinion on so trifling a matter had precipitated a crisis that could scupper the whole works - and that after weeks of arguing with these self-opinionated newcomers about a bizarre teaching scheme dreamed up by an American from ... where was it ... Alaska? What business was it of his? And what did this bunch of people really want? He was frustrated and ready to explode. No committee had seen him like this.

"An impasse, sir," the forlorn Ph.D. had repeated timidly.

"Very well."

Sir Sing-Along's anger had shown in his bristling moustache and the whole set of his heavy body. He had begun to react with the recklessness of a man who sought rapid release from a painful predicament.

"Very well," he had proclaimed, and he had been viewed with amazement: this was not the knight they knew.

Sir Sing-Along had reached deeply into the back pocket of his well-cut pinstriped trousers: they had been newly-pressed that morning. Out had come a brand new European ecu. It was shining, unused, and in mint condition, for the ecu was not to become standard currency in the European Union for another six and a half weeks.

Sir Sing-Along had held the coin aloft for all to see and had then flicked it adroitly high into the air, so high that it had almost touched the finely decorated ceiling of the Education Ministry's second floor committee room before it had fallen back into the chubby hands of the exasperated chairman.

All had craned forward to view the virgin ecu.

"Well?" they had chorused.

The proud head of the President (Elect) of the about-to-be-formed European Union had been uppermost. It stood in sharp relief on Sir Sing-Along's plump palm.

"Well?" the most select committee had chorused again. "Well?"

"They go to university first," the chairman had announced. "The

President-Elect is a university pro-vice chancellor of the greatest administrative merit. That must be an omen."

It had to be. So student tutors of the future were to take their one year university theoretical course before their probationary year with a personal group. It had been decided. But thirty years later there was argument still about the merits of that order and from time to time there were moves to have it changed.

But back in mid-November 1999, despite persistent rumblings, the decision had been accepted. The student who successfully completed the first two years of her course would spend her third year at university, and make frequent visits to tutorial groups. The idea had been that she would prepare, under supervision, a thesis on a topic of her choice - one suggested during her practical work with children in her second year. The intention was that she should become something of an authority in her chosen field. This would add to her confidence, deepen her interest, and enhance the standing of the new profession. The thesis could be prepared at any European university or at an equivalent overseas institution on a student-exchange basis. The latter would be strongly encouraged to enable students to examine cross-cultural elements in the tutoring of young persons.

Susan's own work here had been the writing of a 40,000 word document on possible disincentives to the reading of non-contemporary fiction prevalent among pupils of eleven to twelve years; she had concentrated on the problems caused by authors' use of complex prose. Her study had been acclaimed and a synopsis, with footnotes, had appeared in the English language edition of the *Trans-European Literary Gazette* of June 2023; it had later reappeared as one of a series of occasional pamphlets published to aid tutors working with that age group.

"I think I would want to do something like that," said Patience, "but perhaps not anything quite so highfalutin'."

Susan smiled. She knew the girl meant no disrespect. She touched her arm in a friendly way.

"Well," she said encouragingly, "after your thesis in your third year you'd be nearly home and dry. After the three years - that's three years after getting an honours degree - the student-tutor is awarded provisional recognition as a qualified tutor, and joins a panel for a probationary year. She works for two-thirds of normal fees and is supervised by the panel chairperson who reports on progress to the PTG. Once the association is satisfied with her

93

work, full recognition is accorded."

"It all takes a long time," said Patience as she sat thoughtfully in the comfortable and now well-populated resource centre lounge. "And means lots of hard work."

She occupied the same softly-sprung easy chair that Hildegard Schmidt had taken. The square-shaped room was quiet despite the number of people in it - so effective was its sound insulation - and, although windows were open, little noise came in. Since the potent Noise Abatement Acts of 2006 and 2008, as amended, Britain had become a calmer, quieter, less stressful state.

"It takes the same time as qualifying to be a doctor or lawyer or accountant and the job is just as important. It takes a long time to learn how children can best be brought up and families helped and it is as important as any other professional work."

Patience nodded.

"Anyway," said Susan, "it is well worth it if becoming a tutor is really what you want. It is difficult but fantastically interesting and the time goes quickly. Besides, few qualifications can be worth much if they are easy to obtain. There was too much of that in the past. And tutoring is now highly regarded throughout the Union of European States. If you wanted to, you could tutor anywhere in Europe, especially with English being the first or second language of all children. You would be welcomed everywhere, and that's quite a thought, you know."

"It certainly is," said Patience Payes, rising and ready to go. "So would my saxophone playing, I suppose. I'm quite good, you know." Her face brightened. "And I'm going to play in two jazz bands."

Then she looked at Susan quizzically: "A saxophone is all right, isn't it? As an instrument to offer, I mean?"

Susan grinned, also getting ready to leave. "All right? It would be fantastic. There are plenty of violinists and pianists around. We need a bit of variety. All instruments are welcome."

"How things must have changed since the turn of the Century," said Patience.

"Indeed they have," agreed Susan, "and you don't know a half of it. Come to that, I probably don't know much more myself."

She did not. She did not know, for instance, how very near to defeat the clever Ph.D. had been in mid-November 1999. The select committee had been tired and divided, weary of the entire scheme. His teaching-without-schools proposal had been on the very verge of ignominious collapse. Only the flick of an ecu had saved it.

Talking Over Rutland Water: 2029

The oh-so-sultry senior reporter from Trans-European Super-Documentary TV Networks Incorporated settled herself comfortably and decorously on the low-backed brightly-patterned couch. Wholly relaxed, the trim young woman smiled professionally at the not so young but ever-clever London Ph.D. They were sitting on the spacious sun-deck of his principal holiday home overlooking the broad expanse of Rutland Water. Both were preparing for a thirty-minute interview on the eve of the Ph.D.'s seventieth birthday.

The Ph.D., still slim and with a full head of slowly greying hair, sat opposite his interviewer, his back partly to the Water. He held a scotch and soda lightly in his left hand. The television starlet had a vodka with tonic, while the programme's less-glamorous producer drank chilled apple juice. The two-man camera crew had, already, made deep inroads into several litres of Ruddles' bitter beer.

To the experienced, confident interviewer this assignment posed no problems. It was fees for old rope. She sat calculating how much this was likely to be, with expenses, while she waited for her cue. Then she made an easy start:

"You will be seventy tomorrow," she said with her long-perfected, introductory and meaningless smile, "and ready, I am sure, for a well-earned rest. You will be retiring, no doubt, from the educational scene?"

"I shall write and advise where I can. I shall be available."

"Of course. I was rather taking that for granted. But you are, I think, giving up your official positions?"

"Yes."

"And I am sure I have no need to remind viewers that tomorrow is a significant day not only for you but for the whole of Europe, too?"

The Ph.D. smiled slightly and nodded briefly.

"It will," she said, "be the thirtieth anniversary of the publication of Sir Sing-Along Strain's epoch-making 1999 report on alternative education?"

"Actually it was the report of a most select committee which Sir Sing-Along Strain chaired. The main contents were made known that day, it is true, but the report itself was published officially some months later. At noon on 22nd May, 2000, to be precise."

'Smug devil,' she thought. "How right you are!" she said.

The Ph.D. gestured lightly with open hands. He knew he was. Pleased with the way the interview had opened, he leaned back slightly in his lounger and turned the crystal tumbler in his hand. The scotch was not his favourite blend, but he had been given a whole case the day before by his appreciative American publisher. The celebrated academic had received birthday presents by the score.

"The report recommended, in essence," the young presenter continued, "that a tutorial system should replace both schools and teachers?"

"That is so."

"And really, if we are to be frank, the report was practically all your own work?" She paused, sitting more erect. "Wasn't it?"

She leaned towards him slightly, at the same time smoothing her skirt: it was short in the extreme, tight, and distinctly uncomfortable. And for all that, she feared, the effect was probably wasted. While with some men of seventy there would have been more than a flicker of interest in her movements, with this man there appeared to be immunity.

But there were the viewers to consider: the viewers. Always the viewers and the ratings ... So she crossed her legs again.

"Although it soon became widely known as *The Strain Report of Ninety-Nine,*" she said, "yours was the real brain behind it? You engineered it? The idea was yours?"

"Not entirely. It was a report jointly made by a most industrious select committee working continually against time. Always against time. And yet, despite that effort, it was a most cruelly maligned select committee."

"Aren't most select committees maligned?"

"Not as much as that one."

"And Sir Sing-Along Strain, the chairman, was the most maligned of all?"

"The chairman undertook a task he did not seek and did not want. He completed it with courage within the inadequate time allowed."

"Yet he knew nothing about education?"

The Ph.D. coloured slightly. The camera framed his face so that it filled the viewers' wall-sized screens.

"He was not a professional, political educationalist, if that's what you mean. But in those days that might not have been too great a drawback."

"But the story of him tossing the ecu ..."

"Yes, everyone remembers that. But it was an understandable

recourse - even praiseworthy. There was an exact split on the committee and Sir Sing-Along had no preference. Nor did he consider the issue vital. So he spun a coin and settled the matter. He saved us days of wrangling and the nation considerable time and money."

He did not add that the chairman had probably saved the whole scheme from disintegration.

"Some said it was the best use an ecu has ever been put to?"

"There are cynics everywhere."

"But he was solving educational matters by chance?"

"There are worse ways."

"And chance secured him the chairmanship in the first place? Something about a maiden aunt in Old School Canyon?"

"Creek. Old School Creek. And that is a much vaunted and tastelessly embellished tale. Remember he did not ask for the job. It was foisted on him by an alarmed government and he was far too loyal to his party leader to let him down. Sir Sing-Along had a large estate of rich farmland - not far from here - and he could have retired to it peacefully many years before. He certainly didn't need to put his head on any select committee chopping block."

The reminiscing Ph.D. slowly sipped his birthday scotch.

"But you were the real chairman. You guided him?" the interviewer pressed quietly. "You ran the committee?"

"No. I helped. So did all the other members. None of us was there for fun - although there were a few laughs from time to time."

"At the chairman's expense?"

"You will persist with that line, won't you? The whole select committee was a weird bunch if you believe what the media said at the time. Journalists labelled everyone and cartoons abounded. Satirists penned an easy fortune. According to them there was a crotchety lawyer, a sceptical socialist, a fecund parent-governor . . . a simply dreadful woman of immense wealth who sold cucumbers and canned beans . . . a trade-union leader and an employers' spokesman who seemed to get on suspiciously well together . . . a portly conservative . . . a liberal lady who was pictured as the very archetypal do-gooder . . . The press laughed and sneered at them, misquoted them, played them off one against the other, even doubted their sincerity and motives. Yet they all deserve credit, if credit is what is being handed out on this august anniversary. We should thank them, every one. They did a good job."

He paused and gazed out over the powerful sweep of the immense reservoir. He had grown to love that water. To him it was an inland sea of ever-changing beauty. He turned further and took in a still, tiny, yellow-sailed yacht picked out momentarily by the sun's low rays. The cameramen zoomed purposefully on the yacht, the water, the ageing politician, the whisky, the glass. The viewers would like that. There were even waves rippling on the shore ...

"You see," the Ph.D. continued, "the government of the day was worried about the state of education ..."

"That's putting it mildly?"

"Perhaps. But things had not been happy in the schools for many years under successive governments of varying hues. There was a terrible danger - and I want to be quite emphatic about this - a terrible danger that such a condition would become the norm. It had, by 1999, developed under several diverse, struggling and frequently changing ministers of education ..."

"Secretaries of State?"

"Does it matter? But that second coalition government of 1999, to its credit, wanted to know if there was a viable alternative to schools that could be considered."

"To its credit? Wasn't it simply desperate?"

"Maybe. But it formed a most select committee and that committee came up with one alternative as a possibility. There may have been others then unpublished, who knows? But, as always, there had to be ideas mooted ... that had to be good. Ideas, even if they prove later to be quite impracticable, and even if less radical mortals chortle over them and ridicule the authors, ideas are always needed. Without the flow of new thoughts, new proposals, we stagnate."

"The schools stagnated in 1999?"

"You mustn't put words into my mouth."

This time the clever Ph.D. did not smile. "My view is that in 1999, consideration of alternatives - perhaps radical alternatives - was long overdue. That did not mean that all schools were stagnant or that none was doing good work, but meant that the many teachers who *were* doing good work in a school situation might, in a different environment, do even better. If that were so it would be to the advantage, eventually, of children and their parents, and the state and its teachers. New roads have to be explored, all the time."

"So not all the ..."

"Please let me finish. Too often the suggestion that changes be made is interpreted as an outrageous attack on people working hard in an existing system. Often these people are - as many

98

teachers were then - sensitive folk and some may have taken it the wrong way. Back in 1999 no personal criticism was intended by the select committee. That was, I thought, made perfectly clear at the time. But I have to say that there were plenty of quite nasty verbal and written attacks made on members of the committee. *We* had to put up with them, vile as they were."

"So you..."

"But let's just think about that - about what we are saying. Once upon a time, no doubt, there were many competent drivers of steam engines on the railways and of stage coaches on the roads. Competent or not, both categories of worker had to go; so did the crews of most passenger liners. So did the old-style typesetters in the printing industry. I'm sure the music hall provided highly popular entertainment and had tens of thousands of supporters and hundreds of devoted artists, but the institution became, to all intents and purposes, dead. In the most select committee's view, schools - as an institution - might, similarly, have had their day, or their century! There was a case for suggesting that teaching - as the occupation teaching had become - had had its time. It might, sooner or later, have to go."

"And it did?"

"Yes."

"Sooner?"

"Yes."

"Are you sorry, now, for those teachers who wanted to go on working in the old way in the old system?"

"Sorry? Yes, if that's how it was. Yes, of course I am. I am sorry for most workers whose jobs disappear or who suffer from stressful changes. But sorry that essential changes were made overall in education? No, not sorry at all."

"I see."

The interviewer allowed a pause. She touched little wisps of ash-blonde hair back into place. She knew she should have used more hairspray. She waited, deliberately, for the Ph.D. to continue:

"Anyway, as you will know if you have been well briefed, for years many teachers went on doing precisely that - teaching as they had always done. The government was wise to begin the no-school system in limited and carefully-selected catchment areas with volunteer teachers retraining as tutors and having in their first tutor-groups children whose parents were eager for them to experience the new approach. If I remember correctly, we started with ten resource centres and catered for 12,000 pupils. In the early stages, of course, parents chose between using schools and using the home-based, tutor-assisted scheme for their children."

"And the scheme spread rapidly?"

"Almost beyond the government's ability to cope. It covered most of the country by 2020 and every town and village by 2025."

"And on into Europe?"

"Certainly. It was a coincidence, of course, that the speedy rise of the Union of European States took place at the same time as the no-school movement was gathering pace in Britain. But yes, it is now widespread in Europe and is making great strides in North America, Australia and New Zealand."

"With similar success?"

"From what I have been told on my lecture tours, yes."

"The advantages are universal?"

"Exactly. There is the vastly increased personal care brought about by the child having an individual tutor working closely with the parents and within the family over a long period. This was made possible by the structural changes in the educational system we advised and, simultaneously, by the vast amount of teaching material made available by rapidly developing multi-media and computer-based technology. It was a perfect combination."

He drank more of his liquor: it was not so bad - or perhaps he was simply getting used to it?

"Looking back, what have been the other benefits?" the interviewer asked.

"Simplicity. The old school system had become frighteningly complex and provided many headteachers - and assistants - with administrative nightmares. That was as ridiculous as it was inexcusable. Every moment spent filling in a form or attending a meeting was a moment away from caring for pupils - the very reason the education service existed."

"And?"

"What we did was to say to a tutor: 'Here are your pupils, spend as much time with them as you think fit and organise studies as you think they are needed.' That was the essence of the plan."

"That's all there was to it?"

"Yes. That's all that was needed."

"Just tutor and child and parent?"

"Yes."

"You trusted the tutor?"

"Yes."

"And offered support?"

"Yes. Plenty, and of excellent quality."

"For tutors to use as they thought best?"

"Yes. That is part of the trust."

"And there was the involvement of parents?"

"Yes, very much so. That was crucial."

The Ph.D. thought for a moment.

"All this led, at the same time, of course," he said, "to an enormous enhancement of the professional standing of practising educators - now tutors. Another benefit, equally important, and connected, was the separation, once and for all, of the two quite different facilities offered to parents: those of child education and child supervision."

"By the latter you mean childminding or babysitting?"

The Ph.D. laughed out loud and drained his glass.

"If you say so," he said. "But that division proved to be exceptionally difficult to get across to the public and I regret now that the select committee did not emphasise the need for the separation much more strongly. You do not need and have never needed a highly-trained state-registered nurse to make beds and empty pans, nor do you require and never did require highly-qualified teachers to 'mind' children, mark registers and serve lunch. Nor was it necessary for a child to spend over 27 hours per week in school for eleven years to master the contents of an acceptably comprehensive curriculum; it is certainly not necessary now. Powerful and stimulating teaching aids had been appearing steadily throughout the 1980s and 1990s and have continued apace."

"And the recommendation to separate child education from childminding presented problems? Many problems?"

"Far too many. It became abundantly clear what some parents wanted the schools for. We, that is the select committee, had abusive letters, obscene phone calls and physical threats in only one section of our work, and that was it. But they came, I am sure, from only a tiny, although clamorous, minority."

"Do you have other regrets?"

"Disappointments, perhaps. I had hoped more parents would take seriously and wholly the responsibilities that were set out for them in the National Code of Practice. Most did, of course, and willingly. But a fair-sized proportion were slow to meet their side of the bargain and I am sure we should have asked for the code to be given more bite. The lawyer on the committee always wanted that and I think now he was right."

"Any others?"

"It took a long time for the main political parties to keep their promise not to make political capital out of the education system. That was scandalous and was a main reason why I left my own party and joined the new Progressive People's Party for Universal Peace and Tranquillity, the PPP/UPT."

"That was a good move for you?"

"A good move?"

"Careerwise?"

"I suppose it was. But I did not join for personal promotion. I was beginning to think we needed a new political party as well as a new educational system. Anyway, I joined. That was another exciting time because the PPP/UPT did well in all the elections after 2009 and I moved up with it. When it gained state office I became minister for education early in 2018. By then the new system of tutoring was well established. But later I had no ambition to become Director General of Federal Education - with its Europewide responsibilities."

He noticed that the yacht had moved. It was now much further away. He wondered who the skipper was. A personal friend, perhaps? Old Cadwallader, prolific writer of light romances?

"But going back to an earlier question," he resumed. "An enormous step forward has been the basing of each child's curriculum on literature, music and art for at least the first ten years, and the personalising of that curriculum. When one thinks back, with all the standardisation that was entering man's life, the very last thing we wanted then was a rigid national curriculum for every child, with set subjects and stages and standardised tests."

"Not everyone thought like that?"

"I did."

"And the breaking of all links with work-training and career preparation?" the interviewer prompted.

"That was excellent. Children have now, I am quite sure, much more joy from life and keep their childhood longer; and our society has benefited from the change by seeing a growth in positive values - especially in the caring for others. Most of that has arisen from the ongoing emphasis on teaching through literature."

"If we could change the subject now ..."

"... and end this catalogue of virtues?" The Ph.D. smiled, knowingly.

"Perhaps," said the interviewer. "But, for instance, some teachers didn't make the grade?"

"You mean they did not transfer from teacher role to tutor role easily?"

"Some didn't transfer at all?" suggested the attractive inteviewer. She tossed back her hair to some effect. She did this fifteen minutes into every interview, and expected the camera crew to be ready for the event in order to take a series of advantageous shots. The London Ph.D. noticed, but he was not impressed: he thought the young woman's hair would benefit from an all-round trim.

"There were some who were, perhaps, temperamentally unsuited to making the changes required of them," he agreed. "They were happier working, as they always had worked, with thirty children in a classroom for limited periods of time in a set school day, for a set school year to a set syllabus drawn up by someone else. Yes, there were some like that. Others, nearing retirement, didn't want to retrain. Others still, for various reasons, dropped out and might have done so whatever educational system was introduced."

"Let's be blunt. There was open hostility to the whole scheme."

"Not as much as the media made out. Not much more than there was earlier to selection at eleven plus, or comprehensive education, or mixed ability grouping, or streaming, or raising the school-leaving age, or opting-in or -out, or child-centred education, or testing at key stages, or a national curriculum or formal examinations, or teacher appraisal, or equal pay, or the Burnham Scale. All had their moments, believe me. Especially the Burnham Scale!"

"But they are part of history now . . ."

"And so is the notion of teaching-with-schools. Schools have gone. Teaching-without-schools is here to stay." He emphasised each word by tapping his glass at every syllable. He was adamant.

Then he looked at the young woman thoughtfully and said: "There was very little opposition to our plans, really. Not when you consider the immensity of what we were proposing. You have to keep things in proportion."

"Leading employers were antagonistic to many aspects? They were quite aggressive, in fact. They said a national curriculum was being replaced by a national madness!"

"A few did. There was a suave gentleman on the committee, but we soon calmed him down. Their fears that no specific training for employment in any shape or form for the child's first thirteen years of life would lead to commercial disaster were wholly unfounded. The employees they got eventually were happier, more interesting, more responsible and more amenable people. Employers won hands down!"

"Some headteachers were hostile. So were some administrators. So were some governors."

"And many were not. But, I agree, some got rather agitated. They saw us as destroyers of schools: schools they had worked hard to build up over many years."

"And so you were."

"Were what?"

"Destroyers. Your scheme meant the end of their schools."

"No. Not 'their' schools. They were never 'their' schools. They were the taxpayers' schools - the nation's schools, the people's schools - *our* schools!"

"All right, let's say you destroyed the schools they worked in, administered and governed and were proud of."

"Yes, and let's remember the others, a growing number of others in 1999. Those who were seeking - and taking - early retirement so that they could get out of schools altogether. Figures are available. It was not only assistant teachers who were getting out in droves. For some headship vacancies it was difficult to get an adequate shortlist. It was a problem to fill some governing bodies."

But he seemed uneasy at this line of enquiry. He poured more whisky from the decanter even though it was not of his customary standard. The interviewer let him: it would further loosen his tongue.

It was not only her looks that had enabled her to rise quickly to the top of her profession. She could be relentless in her questioning and merciless in her examination of contentious issues. Her acquired smile belied, for some, her true nature. Now, she sensed the Ph.D.'s discomfort. She closed in.

"There was one almighty row late in 1999 because some headteachers and school governors said they had invited you..."

"You mean the select committee?"

"... had invited the select committee to visit their schools - happy schools - to see good work being done and that you - that is the select committee - did not go?"

"Didn't we? We visited many schools in the very limited time available and agreed that we saw 'good' work in progress, whatever you mean by that. But naturally, they would be the schools we were invited to ..."

"That's ungracious?"

"Not at all. Just a simple statement. Only common sense, really.

Anyway, you could have a full-length TV programme on what was meant by good work in a good school." He waited, then said: "But what we did hear, even in those 'good' schools, was that teachers could have done even better if this, or that, or the other was, or was not available or present or done or not done, or whatever. Let me assure you, there was little complacency."

"I can accept that. I'm sure there are always better ways of doing most things . . ."

"And you have to remember education was in a parlous state. We needn't go through all the ills and conflicts that existed. Just read the educational press of those years - or the general press for that matter. It doesn't make for happy reading. The worst aspect was the sense of disillusionment that existed among many teachers. The presence of those sentiments among the very people who have to inspire and encourage the young of a nation is a threat to the very health of that nation . . ."

"You take that too far . . ." She almost derided him.

"Indeed I do not. And nor did the most select committee. They believed that only a completely new start would disperse that disillusionment. And for a completely new start the schools themselves had to go."

"It is said you were completely obsessed by that idea?"

"I stand by what has happened."

"But you were obsessed? You had something against schools?"

"No. I simply thought they were obsolete. The time for change had come."

"And you were exceptionally lucky with the timing?"

"Do you mean it was fortunate that at the very time the new ideas were coming in the rapidly-developing technology was making practicable our quite revolutionary proposals and making viable the new ideas?"

"That is what I mean," she stressed.

"Then yes, we were lucky."

"And were the ideas so new?"

"What does *that* mean?"

"Well, the Open University had provided excellent distance learning for decades, so had the Australians, through radio teaching, and the BBC, ITV and others. Correspondence colleges had existed since the nineteenth century. A tutorial system for teaching undergraduates had been in vogue at Oxford and Cambridge since the Middle Ages. The notion of teaching the future generation by means of classical literature had been around for a millennium, and the idea of the tutor-mentor sitting with students at his feet went back to Greek and Roman times. Many parents already taught their children at home and avoided schools. Even moderately wealthy families had pre-empted your proposals and employed nannies, governesses and tutors for their precious offspring..."

For a few moments the young interviewer, allowing herself to be carried along by her theme, exposed her own feelings. The canny Ph.D. would not let that pass.

"I am delighted to have had such fine antecedents," he beamed.

"That is all you have to say?"

"What more is there? I am reassured now, and I would have been reassured then."

"*You* would have been reassured?"

"The most select committee itself would have been reassured, of course."

"Of course. As you reminded me, you were not the power behind the throne."

The elderly but still politically nimble Ph.D. smiled but did not respond. The persistent interviewer tried yet again. She was determined to make him reply to the criticism that what had been done in 1999 was nothing new.

"And home-based education?" she continued. "During the Nineties many parents, or families, were opting out of the school system and educating their children at home, and the numbers were growing significantly month by month. The evidence was there for all to see - or at least there for those who wanted to see? You merely developed what they were already doing?"

"I am happy to agree with that if it's what you want. No doubt those families were in the very vanguard of the teaching-without-schools movement." He thought carefully and chose his words deliberately; "But despite your exclamations, they were a small minority. They might have been joined by many more if the legal position of home-educating had been more widely understood, but even so, we are talking of relatively small numbers. What we did was point the way to the national possibility of dispensing with schools if that was what was needed. If, incidentally, we helped the people already teaching their children at home - by offering a variety of approaches and resources - then that was excellent. But the committee was concerned with the practicalities of a massive change that would affect all families - millions of them. So, I adhere to my claim that the committee made quite revolutionary proposals and that when those proposals were put into effect the changes in family life and the nation's health were revolutionary, too."

The Ph.D. sat back, content with his answer.

The interviewer changed tack. This man was no walkover.

"Some points you lost, though, didn't you?" she challenged.

"Such as?"

"The original proposal that all entrants to the new profession should have an arts degree - and one in literature, at that."

"I never expected the English literature only requirement to go through intact. I was flying a kite."

"But that's what you wanted? What you would have liked?"

"Yes."

"It was said you were obsessed with that idea, too? That because it was your teaching subject and the theme of your doctorate, you thought every child should be taught everything through literature? You were paddling your own canoe?"

"That was one of the cheaper remarks of the time."

"But you believed in it?"

"Yes, I did. I thought, quite simply, that all could benefit from the study of literature. I still do. Of all subjects open, readily, to all people, I consider it to be the one which deals, universally and intimately, with human life and its prospects, predicaments and possibilities, and that, to me, is what the education of children is all about. But I did not propose that all a child's time be spent on literature, which is what some trouble-making journalists and antagonistic educationists implied."

"But you now accept that there is much more to life than literature? That children have to learn, experience, feel, grasp, explore, discover, calculate, test, far more than that? Far more?"

"Much of that can come through the study of a wide range of literature - ancient and modern - but, in its general sense, yes, I accept what you say."

"Yet you did want all entrants to teaching - that is, to tutoring - to have a B.A. degree. You lost that point?"

"Eventually, and only after a prolonged battle. The most select committee, as a whole, saw the merit of such a course ..."

"Which was?"

"For one thing they were greatly impressed by the argument that Britain's culture is rich in the arts. Our record of producing leading works in many spheres is second to none. They recognised that overseas interest in our authors, artists, playwrights, sculptors, musicians is worldwide and immense and that . . ."

". . . if we couldn't sell them anything else we could at least offer them hefty slabs of culture. We could sell our heritage?"

"I would not put it quite like that and I think you might know what I mean when I say that the whole British Commonwealth has a cultural legacy to be proud of. It must be preserved and for that to be ensured all our children need to know about it and be immersed in it. That means that the tutors' own, personal education and professional training need to be strongly influenced by it. It cannot be left to chance. The committee recognised the inescapable logic of that . . ."

"But not Parliament?"

"It went through the Commons."

"Only with a struggle and because many M.P.s then were arts graduates themselves?"

"You cannot prove that - and it is a slur on the Members."

"The Lords threw it out. They would not have it at any price. They shouted defiance. Some said it was the only good thing they did that year?"

"They did not 'throw it out', as you put it. They sent the Bill back with the recommendation that a new degree, a B.C.S., be offered to students and accepted for entry to the emerging profession."

"But it is not what you wanted. It was to be in three parts?"

"It was . . . and it is. Three parts of equal standing. First, literature pure and simple; second, one from a selection of music, art, drama etc.; third, any other university-offered subject of the student's choosing. That makes the Bachelor of Combined Studies: the B.C.S."

"So that the student who, at age eighteen, hoped to become a tutor in early education and had an interest in one of the sciences, for instance, could make that the third element of her degree?"

"Yes."

"And still have something extra to fall back on if, in the end, she did not tutor?"

"Yes."

"And she would have much more to offer a tutor panel if she did go ahead?"

"That was the claim."

"But you and your supporters in the Commons did not fight?"

"Time was too short. It would have been a disaster to have sent the Bill back with the Lords bogged down with the debate on proportional representation. It would have been lost for years."

"The government was nervous in other ways. It rejected parts of *The Strain Report* ?"

"Such as?" asked the wary Ph.D.

"It decreed the school system be kept for parents who needed it. The two systems had to run in tandem."

"They had to anyway. It was impossible to change everything overnight." The Ph.D. shrugged his shoulders. "They said the systems had to run together for twenty years, but, as I anticipated, the tutorial system dominated within ten. The important thing is parents had a choice - not between school and school, but between school and a real alternative."

"And some still use the schools . . ."

"About as many as educated their children at home in 1999."

The unruffled Ph.D. helped himself to cashew nuts.

"But you, yourself, were unhappy about the new state system of tutoring being wholly secular?" pursued the interviewer.

"Yes, but that was a personal concern of mine - and others."

"And that one you definitely lost. You gave in?"

"No, what I said at the time was that the matter should have had much greater debate. I think it was rushed through partly because of the time element again, but mainly because the committee was afraid. The chairman was certainly apprehensive."

"He was under fire from all sides?"

"He told me it was worse than anything he had endured in a distinguished - if brief - military career."

"You, yourself, were one of twenty signatories to a letter in *The Times* arguing that the 'values' you proposed in your curriculum construction - such as love, honesty, trust, reliability, etc. - were all contained in the Christian faith . . ."

". . . and the same letter accepted that the holders of other faiths would make similar claims regarding their own teaching. The signatories said that, in view of this, the curriculum should not be based on the teachings of one, named, chosen, faith. It would have to be secular. Because of my own beliefs I found it a hard course to propose and so did many others. But we hoped parents would be able to approach the curriculum - which is not fixed, remember - in such a way that it accorded with their persuasion . . ."

"If they have one . . ."

"Of course," the Ph.D. almost snapped. "With the help of the tutors of their choice they should be able to do that."

"Tutors of their own religion?"

"That is a matter for them."

"But the move to put British education on the same secular footing as in the USA caused an uproar. You can't deny that?"

"I have no wish to. I was in the middle of it. But I am sure now, the severity of the discord being such as it was, that the right decision was made. We had to go secular. It was impossible to meet all the demands of so many diverse groups and hope for harmony. Also, I feel, new education system or not, and teaching-without-schools or not, this was an issue that had to be faced and I think the result would have been the same. The whole area was becoming fraught with problems in 1999, regardless of the select committee."

"There was some deliberate, vicious, mischief-making?"

"I'm afraid there was."

"There was one particular socialist on the committee who . . ."

"Oh, he . . ."

"Yes . . ?"

"He was a member of the committee and entitled to his views," said the Ph.D. hastily and despite the strain he was feeling as the interview progressed. But he had almost made a slip.

The well-known TV interviewer smiled and slid gracefully along the couch. She tucked one shapely leg under the other and adopted a favourite pose. She straightened the collar of her blouse and caressed her elegant neck. The sun had gone from Rutland Water and hidden lights had been activated to aid the cameras. The clever Ph.D. was interested but showing signs of weariness. The past few days had been full for him and something of an ordeal. The practised journalist prepared to end the interview. If her subject appeared tired on screen she might, by those colleagues who loved her not, be accused of harassing a notable septuagenarian. She was far too smart to fall into that trap. She knew how many wanted her job and, moreover, who most of them were.

"Do you visit tutor groups and resource centres now, even though your work is done?" she asked in softer tones.

"My work is not done. It is true I am now retiring from the state legislature, but I shall still write - and even give TV interviews! And yes, I do visit tutors and talk to them. In fact I help quite frequently with a tutor panel - one at Market Harborough to be exact."

"That's good to hear."

"My youngest grandson is nine and is in a tutor group there. I'm helping the group prepare a visit they are planning to Roman remains in Monmouth, Caerleon and Caerwent. I shall go with them and talk about those aspects with which their tutor is unfamiliar."

"Unfamiliar? Is she newly qualified?"

"Oh, no. She's twenty-nine and working with her third personal group. She's an excellent tutor. Her new Border Country project is linked to the reading of tales of life in Roman Britain. The literature is authentic and stimulating and the National Media Library has recently revised its relevant material. The work is planned for children from several groups and is imaginative and constructive - like that of all our personal tutors. Susan's work is no exception."

"Susan?"

"Susan Smith - the tutor."

"Do you know Susan well?"

"Quite well."

"Do you talk to her about the old school-based teaching?"

"Sometimes."

"What does she say?"

The interviewer spoke kindly now. This was the sort of interview that had to be ended on a friendly, sympathetic, even celebratory note. The time for cross-examination had passed. An appropriate smile would be maintained for the remainder of the programme.

"She learned a lot about it years ago from a university lecturer," the Ph.D. explained. "I think she takes it with a pinch of salt. Anything I add she probably ascribes to my fantasising."

"Is she right to do that?"

"Perhaps that's a question for the interviewer to answer!"

"Point taken." The young woman beamed. She had readily conceded a point she would have disputed only ten minutes before. She appeared yielding, warm and informal. She had finished her vodka some time ago and hoped to be offered another. She would like to chat further with this man when the interview was over. There was much more to him than at first appeared and she thought his holiday home was quite delightful and so picturesquely placed.

A selection of outside shots would have made a spectacular lead in to her programme, but the crew had been late arriving and the opportunity had been missed. Now there was no light at all on Rutland Water. The reservoir was still and dark: the sun had long set and the moon had not yet risen . . . she ought to be able to work some of that into her script . . .

"Let's leave it there," she said softly. "Let me thank you, not only for this quite fascinating interview, but for all your work in education over what has been almost half a century. And especially we must thank you for that vital task you undertook thirty years ago . . ."

"Please don't thank me. Thank the gentleman who was my colleague and who became my friend, the committee's chairman, Sir Sing-Along Strain. Without his guidance we would have lost our way. He kept the committee moving inexorably on a road that was long and often rough. But he made sure we reached our destination. There was much more to him than at first appeared . . ."

With difficulty the interviewer kept back a laugh.

"And thank all the other members of that most select of committees," he said. "Everyone contributed . . . well . . ."

For the briefest of moments the clever, now expensively-bespectacled Ph.D. pictured the argumentative, sceptical socialist, and frowned. But the image quickly faded. Charity prevailed . . . and, anyway, the man of the left had made them pause and think. He had had his own perspective.

"Yes," he confirmed quietly. "Thank them all."

Then, unsure of herself for the very first time that evening, the interviewer hesitated. She spoke almost in an undertone:

"But they are all . . . dead? Dead long ago?"

The renowned Ph.D. regarded her sadly. She was so young. She knew so little. Then his tired face brightened and, as if to emphasise his next remarks, he leaned forward slightly and touched a nylon-covered knee:

"Ah, but their work isn't, is it?" he said confidingly. "Their work isn't. Not by a long chalk!"